Dr Laxmi Kathuria is the granddaughter of Biggy, the subject of this book. Early stardom came when she appeared in the BBC drama 'River City'.

She now works as a psychiatrist with children and young people and has worked as an onscreen psychiatrist for Channel Four in their series 'Beauty & the Beast; Ugly Face of Prejudice'.

Laxmi lives in Glasgow with her husband and four cats.

Dear Kathy

All my love Andy & Always

Laxmi xxx

Biggy – Kee Khenda

The Difficulties in dealing with Dementia

by
Dr Laxmi Kathuria

with Sue Reid Sexton

Indigo Dreams Publishing

First Edition: Biggy – Kee Khenda

First published in Great Britain in 2014 by:
Indigo Dreams Publishing Ltd
24, Forest Houses
Halwill
Beaworthy
Devon
EX21 5UU
www.indigodreams.co.uk

ISBN 978-1-909357-38-9

A CIP record for this book is available from the British Library.

Designed and typeset in Minion Pro by Indigo Dreams.
Cover design by Ronnie Goodyer of Indigo Dreams.
Photographs used with permission from the Kathuria family.

Printed and bound in Great Britain by Imprint Academic, Exeter.
*Papers used by Indigo Dreams are recyclable products made from wood grown
in sustainable forests following the guidance of the Forest Stewardship
Council.*

**All royalties received by the author from this book will be donated to
Alzheimer's Society to help fund and support the research into and
treatment of dementia.**

For my mum, Rita, and my Granddad, Papa Ji

Acknowledgements

Thanks go to Sue Reid Sexton in the preparation of the original manuscript.

Sue Reid Sexton is the author of *Mavis's Shoe*, a novel about the Clydebank Blitz of 1941, and *Rue End Street*, the sequel (due out May 2014). Her short stories and poetry have also been published widely in many journals. With a background in social care and trauma counselling, she lives and works in Glasgow, Scotland, and is currently working on a variety of fiction and non-fiction projects of her own and for other people. Her website can be found at www.suereidsexton.com

This work is also dedicated to the memory of Rita Steward, who walked this way too.

Biggy – Kee Khenda

Prologue

What's actually happening here? If this was an animal we would have put her down by now. She's suffering, we are all suffering. She's gone – each day she goes a little more. There is no other way out of this – no miracle cures. Just one consequence.

Human beings? We may have evolved but we have no common sense.

Oh my fucking God – I can't believe I'm thinking this let alone writing it down. At the first sign of trouble – put them down? Let's see anyone try that with you, you selfish bitch.

I took the Hippocratic Oath – I uphold a standing. First, to do no harm. Harm to whom? You will harm everyone and everything if you carry on thinking like this. Just shut up and man up.

Am I the only one who feels like this? I don't want to see her. I don't have time for this. I can't handle this. You visit her and it's the same old crap – same old questions, same lectures.

When you were a kid, how many times did she listen to you asking the same questions over and over again – and did she shout at you once? Don't have time, Miss High and Mighty? Too big to care? Fuck you.

What's wrong with you? Reflect on this, analyse it, feel it. You are clearly scared – it's a defence mechanism at work here. You use denial and humour and distance. This is what the rest of them are all doing too. Ask for help.

Fuck you and your psycho-babble. Save it for the day job. I can't deal with this right now. You think you're the only one dealing with this? Can you imagine the queues of people outside their GP's if we all started blubbing at the thought of doing some hard work?

I hate her – she brought this on herself. If you move to a country, you learn its ways and you integrate. You don't get to a stage where you lose your mind and then expect everyone else to pick up the pieces and suddenly you need people who can speak your language, cook your food, and understand your culture. Maybe you should have thought about this before you came to the UK.

What? Dementia isn't caused by someone not using their brain. It's not her fault. Would you say this to someone who has cancer? You wouldn't even think it. Yet this is somehow her fault? Disgusting – absolutely disgusting.

I want my Big Mama. I need her here. She still has so much to see, so much to do. Don't give up on us Biggy. Try to remember. If you try really hard I know you will remember. Look into my eyes. I'm looking into yours, trying to convince myself that I can see a flicker of hope.

This is an emotional warning. This is how I, the author of this book, feel about dementia because dementia is as confusing for those around her as it is for the demented.

This book is mostly about Big Mama, my Gran, sometimes known as Biggy, or even just Big. Although Big Mama is the person who has been diagnosed with dementia, this story is also about some of the rest of the family. We all need to stick together. We all need and want to do what's best for Biggy.

But along the way, the sufferer, in this case Biggy, has had less and less of a voice about what's happening until finally she has almost no say at all. At the same time everybody else can be very vocal and lucid about what they think she needs or what needs to be done and as a result there can be utter chaos amongst the family. It's like a black hole of calm which is often difficult to even contemplate.

Human beings are supposed to know how to care. Caring is supposed to come naturally, or at least that's what I've always thought. So why is it then that being a carer is so incredibly hard? I've got all these voices inside my head, perhaps you do too, and sometimes I think I'm the one that's going mad and not Big Mama, not Biggy my indomitable Gran.

I don't really know if we're allowed to talk about these things, or indeed if we should talk about these things, or even if it's fair to talk about these things. But dementia is something that, while it's not a physical cancer, is however cancerous. It seems to eat away at absolutely everybody and it's not just the person who is affected that's suffering: it's everybody around about them.

As dementia is becoming more and more common, I'm

certain that there are more and more families, more and more people, who are left with these voices inside their heads that they can't make sense of. It's kind of like confusion by proxy.

It's an illness and a situation which is difficult to imagine if you're not experiencing it or even to make sense of if you are. Writing this book has been incredibly hard. Every thought, whether it's a confused thought from Big Mama or a lucid one from me (or the amalgamation of the two) comes somewhere between confusion and clarity. What you end up with is only an interpretation. This then has had to be translated into a book. And it's almost impossible to express the thoughts and the feelings which go with all this because it happens so quickly. I just don't understand why it's so difficult but it feels like trying to catch grains of sand as they run through your fingertips.

Big Mama, my Gran, used to say to me, and my mum still says this to me, that there's no right time to have children. I don't have children but when a child comes into this world you enjoy seeing them learn and you enjoy them picking up new understanding or abilities and making sense of the world. This is why it is so tragic when, at the other end of the spectrum, someone is becoming more and more child-like and unlearning all the thoughts, feelings, memories and personality that they have accumulated through the years.

It doesn't just happen overnight of course but it seems to feel like one minute you've got your loved one, and the next minute you've just got bits of them. Not only that but those fragments are kind of being blown away by the wind. You're losing bits of a person that you used to love and you've got no way of teaching them how to get it all back. And although it doesn't really matter sometimes, in the general run of things, what day it is, what month it is, or even what year it is, we can become so consumed by these little facts that they can take over our entire conversation with our demented relative. You wind up with 'What day is it? What month is it?' again and again until your own sense of time and your presence as part of the problem become so paramount that you can't think of anything else.

While we're on the subject of time, it stops, but simultaneously also goes unimaginably fast. You lie awake at night thinking about your relative and you lie awake at night worrying about all the sadness and the guilt and all the other feelings that go with those, and the sense of loss. And then you sit and you think, 'I wonder how Big Mama's doing in that nursing home?' Is she feeling lost? Does she even remember that she's lost? Which bits of her is she trying to cling on to? And then that transition between not being demented and being demented, did she know? And was she absolutely terrified that she was losing herself?

There was nothing that we could do to stop it.

I don't know how she is in that nursing home. And I don't know how she's feeling at night-time when there's nobody else there. And I don't know how she feels when she wakes up in the morning absolutely terrified that she's in a place she doesn't recognise. And I don't know how to help her.

So this takes me back to my original point: you're supposed to be able to care. Caring is supposed to come naturally to human beings. Love is unconditional. But in reality, as more and more of us become carers, more and more of us have to try and make sense of this situation, and this means that an increasingly number of us are affected by this 'cancer' of dementia which eats away at everybody. For me it feels like we no longer have a future, not one that we can contemplate with the person who we all knew. So we're doing reminiscence therapy, we're all going back in time with the result that we're all getting stuck in the past.

As well as all of this, the more of the past Big Mama starts to forget, the further back we have to go. But there's a bit that I don't know. I don't know how far back she's going to go. Is she going to forget us? Is she going to forget her Grand-children? Is she going to forget her children? And where do we stand with that? We can only associate our memories with what we've lived through. The rest is just a story.

It's that sense of helplessness that's made the writing of this book so important. Dementia is going to affect one in two of us in the next generation. It's the next big thing. My mum is absolutely terrified that she's going to get it too and I'm terrified that I'm going to have to be a carer all over again. But why would I be so terrified? My Gran not only raised my mum, she also raised me, and helped me through so much. I find this a huge burden, a huge chore and a huge challenge. Read this book and I'll try to explain.

There are no heroes in this story. There aren't any saviours. There is no happy ending. This book is just about making sense of us, of our experience of this, of what's happening around about us all, and perhaps offering some kind of support and hope to anyone who is going through this now. There are probably millions of families out there who may be coping better or worse or somewhere in between. But stuck right in the middle of all these coping strategies and these emotions is a person who's fading away. It's happening so quickly yet, at the same time, so slowly that sometimes it's hard to know whether we're keeping up or running ahead.

Writing this book is important for me as a way of celebrating Big Mama's life: my hero, my support and my friend, always there in the background, apparently clueless but still applauding me as I go on. It's about appreciating where she is with all of this. It's about trying to understand who she was and it's about letting go so that we can go through this journey with her, wherever it's going to take us all, in a supportive frame of mind, for her and for us.

This story is also about my mum, the strongest woman I know: a fighter, a trooper, a survivor, the voice of reason and of madness, the counsellor, the rock and the next Big Mama to my children. It is hard to stand by and watch your mum suffer. I don't want it to happen again.

Chapter 1

The Kathuria and Verma family are gathered for a special Mother's Day meal and Big Mama, otherwise known as Biggy, is special guest of honour. We all want Big Mama, my Gran, to have a special day. We want her to be part of the family again. We want her to enjoy being out with the family for the evening and hope that taking her to one of her favourite restaurants will bring her back to us and prove there is really nothing wrong with her. Family means everything to us – Biggy taught us that: unity, togetherness, dignity.

We're also there because we aren't seeing enough of Biggy – us kids that is – though I suppose we're not kids any more. There are five of us and we range between eighteen and thirty in age. Like some glamorous party club! Though I must admit, I'm getting a bit too old for the other four's energy! I wish my sister, Deepa was there. She always knows how to cheer Biggy up, always knows the right thing to say. I sometimes forget she is my kid sister and not the elder, with her wise shoulders. I think she is secretly Biggy's favourite – and rightly so. She's always had time for Biggy, unlike me.

'You need to spend more time with your Gran,' my mum kept saying.

'We need to do more things as a family.' That's my Auntie Anju, or Anju Masi as we call her. 'Keep the circle going, the family traditions.'

'We're all going for a big family meal,' they said, both of them.

'You organise it.'

So we, the kids, decided to book Chillies in the West End. We decided to make a right good effort so it would be something very memorable.

'I hate Indian food!' complained Raj, my brother.

'Don't be a moaning Minnie,' cousin Preity said grinning at me. She knows I hate Indian food too.

'But there's no booze,' said cousin Dhruv.

'I would kill for a bottle of red wine and a straw,' I said. 'But this is not about me or you. It's for Biggy and the mums, and Chillies do their kind of food. And Biggy doesn't drink. So, no slipping her sneaky brandies to keep her quiet!'

'We would never do that!' they said. I felt a pang of guilt. It had crossed my mind, and my mum's too. It horrifies me to say it out loud, but I've often thought that a drink helps calm everyone down. It's certainly provided me, Anju Masi and Mum with a few moments of light relief in recent months. But Biggy has her principles, has had them all her life. She's never had a drop of alcohol, not one, and doesn't know what that feels like. I wonder what it's like to have principles ... coping mechanisms ... inner strength.

Preity booked a table for eleven people at seven o'clock. Again – my baby cousin yet still so organised. Chillies is just down from Biggy's sheltered flat too so it should have been easy.

But no. Most of us are sitting round the table. We're a noisy lot and we had plenty to celebrate, not least my engagement to my dearly beloved, Stephen. That had been one of our last family gatherings, the big engagement party, and my Gran had surprised us all. Anju Masi (my mum's younger sister but in all honesty my second mum) organised it. That woman could organise anything from a piss up in a brewery to a Bollywood extravaganza. With minimum effort, no complaining and some style! Oh, and a wee bit of bossiness! We'd hired a big hotel for it, done it "Asian style" with thrones and Indian food and music and invited an hundred guests, mostly friends. Everyone was there. But Biggy hadn't wanted to go. I think she was nervous or something. Anyway, not only did Mum and Anju manage to get her there on time, but we even managed to persuade her out onto the dance floor. She was out there giving it laldy to all this bhangra. She was hilarious. She danced all night, completely lost in the music and kept everyone entertained, and then we couldn't get her to stop. She wouldn't come off the dance floor. She was totally mental, and then afterwards she wouldn't go to bed. Of course all this was to the great delight of my friends who still talk about it and think she's the cutest, most amazing thing ever.

'It's time to go to bed,' said my mum. 'The DJ stops at midnight.'

'No, no,' said Biggy. 'I'm still up. I'm still happy partying.'

And this after she'd refused to get ready and said she didn't want to come and my poor mum had to coax and cajole and all the rest of it.

So we weren't too alarmed when on this occasion, at Chillies, she and my mum were late.

Not that we were bored waiting. There's always plenty to talk about. The boys were discussing workouts and muscle-building supplements and the girls were looking at photos on the laptop and resisting the temptation to tell them to shut up.

Stephen's parents were there too and I was taking the micky out of his dad, telling them all the designer gear they'd have to buy me for the wedding. Like a reverse dowry. Biggy would have been horrified if she'd heard. She likes the simple life.

'I'd like a Ferrari or four,' I said. 'There are so many important people coming. You, for instance.'

Anju's mother-in-law was there. Her name is Nani Maa and we all call her Gran too even though she's not really everyone's Gran. Nani Maa is the same age as Biggy but different in every way. For a start she looks like the queen so I always greet her with a curtsy and call her Queenie.

'How's your cooties?' she says. So we all fall about laughing. Cooties is 'bitches' in Punjabi. She means my super-cute cats.

'The bitches are fine,' I say.

Nani Maa wants to know the best things to eat to keep her brain ticking over, although she's all there, sharp as a tack. She always has some story to tell. She reassures Stephen's dad that I only need a few hundred guests for the wedding, but really we need six big shiny cars, then winks at me while she watches their jaws drop.

The waiting staff want us to order. Time is rolling on. Biggy's flat is only round the corner. I'm starting to get worried. Guilt is creeping in. It's always down to my mum or Anju to get Big Mama ready and it's not been an easy task recently. Just as we're about to give up on them – ta-dah! – here they are at last.

Mum's face is red and we can see she's had a struggle. A 'face like fizz' is what you might call it.

'Namaste!' beams Biggy to the assembled company.

Everyone stands up for kisses and hugs with Big Mama. She smiles serenely in a sari of pure gold and greets everyone like Lady Muck. Preity takes her coat and we all admire the sari and the sparkly cardigan she's wearing over it. 'Namaste,' she says again and pinches Preity's cheek. She goes to sit down between Nani Maa and Raj because she always sits next to Nani Maa and because Raj has a treat for her.

'Kiddha! How're you doing?' says Raj and slaps her on the back.

She reaches up to him. 'Come for some pyaar, some love,' she says, laughing and yanks him down to her level for a kiss.

'She wouldn't get dressed,' says my mum with a scowl and plumps down in the chair beside mine. 'She point blank refused. I'm standing there in the hall and ...' She shakes her head to indicate she simply can't go on. But she can: 'She was accusing me of all sorts. It'd make your ears burn. She kept saying "You think I'm Pagal?" You think I'm mad? She wouldn't believe you were all here waiting. Said I was taking her to the loony bin. I kept telling her 'It's on the calendar. See?'

She and Biggy stare at each other. 'Mother's Day,' she says. 'On the calendar and circled in red.' She shrugs. 'Red,' she says for extra emphasis. 'Oh my God, have I had enough! Wish we'd gone somewhere else now. I need a brandy.' Then a minute later: 'Naked!' she whispers to me so I'm the only one who can hear. I've no idea what she's talking about. She can't possibly mean Biggy was naked. Naked isn't what Biggy does.

Everyone rearranges themselves round the table and the

waitress hovers again, pad poised, waiting for everyone to stop talking.

'Order! Order!' says Preity.

'Good idea!' says Dhruv.

Everyone is there, but this meal is really the work of my mum and my aunt Anju. They always try to keep the family together, they never give up. It's a 'do or die' sort of occasion. We all watch out for Big Mama and include her when we can, even though our conversation is mainly in English. We all talk English to each other and then we'll say the odd thing to Big Mama in Punjabi to keep her in the loop. Punjabi is her language and she only speaks enough English to get by, get her shopping in and so on. And because she is the person who mostly brought me up, I am fully bi-lingual. Doesn't mean I always choose to speak to her in Punjabi. I feel awkward sometimes – I don't know why.

Big Mama announces she has already eaten.

'I'm not hungry,' she protests. 'I ate only half an hour ago. Don't order anything for me.'

'Rubbish,' says my mum, throwing her hands up.

'But this is Chillies,' we tell Biggy. 'Have a little something. It's your favourite. They've got dhaal the way you like it and saag paneer, almost as good as your own.'

'Don't be silly,' she says. 'It'll all go to waste. I've eaten. I'm telling you. You just go ahead. I'll just sit and watch.'

So we order a mountain of rotis, all kinds of dhaal and oodles of saag paneer, enough for her too because it's what she likes and we're doing it her way and because we've seen this move before. Raj, of course, stubbornly orders hot American wings for starters followed by roast grilled non-spicy chicken, declaring his gym routine will be upset if he doesn't, not to mention his digestive system. He doesn't know that I saw the pizza boxes in his room the other night though – I plan on keeping that secret to use against him at the appropriate time.

It's a busy night, what with their being so many of us. Biggy asks everyone how they are, whether they're enjoying their jobs? Most of us grunt, yes or no in return, but my mum and my aunt Anju want to make sure Biggy is having fun and feels part of it. So we give her a running commentary on what everyone's saying. She eats every last scrap of her dhaal and polishes off a very large portion of saag paneer. Rasmalai, a creamy Indian pudding, is on its way, along with fruit pakora for me.

'Fruit pakora?' they all say in disbelief. 'Are you sure, Pinky?' Pinky isn't my real name. It's what the family call me, and close friends. Biggy wanted it to be my real name but my dad said no. I think it might have been cute being Dr Pinky!

Coffee is coming too and half a cup of tea for Biggy. Nani Maa, my other Gran, asks Biggy about her day centre, the people there, are they nice, has she made new friends? Nani Maa has a worried look about her. Then she asks me whether she should eat the Rasmalai or not. The more she sees of Biggy, the more she worries about her own health. She thinks all this sugar will slow down her brain function and asks my professional medical opinion. I tell her to go ahead, that happiness is good for her, and I'm pleased to be asked. The boys are showing her some stretch moves to help keep her back straight, right in the middle of the restaurant. I wonder if Stephen's family know what they are letting themselves in for. My mum and Aunt Anju are in some kind of earnest discussion, probably about Big Mama. Stephen and his parents are still talking about wedding preparations and Stephen, who knows that in truth we want a simple wedding, is keeping the panic-factor going. When I say "we" I mean "he".

Raj has brought out his laptop. He has spent days putting all the old family photos on it so he can show them to Big Mama and jog her memory of the past. I couldn't believe he had done that. I could see Mum and Anju looking at him with pride. Preity is standing behind Raj looking at them too, although most are from before her time. She actually looks like a young Biggy –I hadn't seen it before until now.

'Who's this then,' says Raj. And they all peer in at the screen.

Biggy squints at it too.

'Come on then,' says Raj. 'Who's that?'

'I know who that is,' says Big Mama. 'You tell me. I don't have to tell you. I already know who that is.'

'Tell us then,' says Preity.

'It's … it's Anju of course. That's my wee Anju Ji,' says Big Mama.

'Are you playing silly games with me?' says Raj. He says this in his best Punjabi accent because his actual Punjabi isn't up to it and he thinks just saying it with a Punjabi accent like hers will help her understand. He once went round the whole of India speaking Punjabi-style English with a Punjabi accent until someone pointed it out to him. He'd no idea he was doing it. He still doesn't know half the time, until we all do it back to him to wind him up.

24

'It's Anju,' insists Big Mama with a glance at me then a frown.

'No,' says Raj. 'It's Dhruv when he was wee. Don't you know your own Grandson? Dhruv – Biggy thinks you look like a girl!' Dhruv pulls a face.

'I knew that,' says Big Mama. 'I was only kidding.' And she smiles up at him. 'Show me another one.'

Stephen and his parents are watching. They're very sensible people, very correct, but they like a good laugh too, same as the rest of us, so I decide to have some fun.

'Billy Connolly Kee khenda?' I say. 'What does Billy Connolly say?' We all turn to Biggy smiling expectantly. 'Come on, Big Mama, what does Billy Connolly say?' I repeat. She looks up at me and her smile freezes. We have done this a million times before. We've done it for over two decades since I was nine and sitting in her house eating pizza on a Saturday night. Big Mama knows her part. We wait for her to play it.

But she stares up at us and the smile falters.

'Billy Connolly Kee khenda?' I repeat. 'Come on. ਵੁਟ ਦੇਏਸ ਤੇ ਸੀ/'

There's a pause. No-one says a word. The smiles are still there. We wait.

'Come on, Big Mama, you know the answer,' I say. 'What does Billy Connolly say?'

'It's embarrassing, Pinky. Stop it,' says Anju, glancing at Stephen's parents.

There's a pause.

'I'm not doing it,' says Big Mama, and she folds her hands on her lap.

'What comes next?' I say, ignoring this. It's part of the game. She's just being shy, or so I think. Maybe I'm just hoping.

There is a silence and Big Mama's smile fades away. She glances down the table. Dhruv fumbles with his phone as if there's some really important message he has to attend to.

'You're taking the piss out of her,' says my mum.

Biggy looks at her like she doesn't understand.

'Billy Connolly Kee khenda?' I laugh. 'Come on, Biggy. What's the matter with you?'

'Leave her,' says Anju. 'She doesn't want to.'

'She's not a performing monkey,' says my mum.

'I know that,' I protest. 'She knows what to say, don't you Gran? Just say it. Go on. You know you're going to.'

'I'm not,' says Biggy. 'Whatever it is, I'm not doing it.' She sits up straight and shifts in her chair, toying with a table napkin. There's no smile now.

Every other time we've done this you just can't stop her once you've got her started. Once she's doing her Billy Connolly impersonation she'll be at it all night and the place will be in an uproar.

'You want me to do it for you? Will I? Will I do it?' I say.

'Leave her, Pinky,' says Anju. 'It's rude. It's not for company.' She nods at Stephen's parents who are wondering what is going on, still smiling in that encouraging way of people who don't know the danger they're in.

'No, no, no,' says Biggy. 'I'm not doing it, whatever it is. I'm not doing it.'

26

There's a brief shocked silence ... *Whatever it is?* We all talk at once to cover the awful realisation that Big Mama has forgotten her part. She's lost what Billy Connolly says, her part of what we've been doing for years. I catch eyes with my mum.

'Here's another one,' Raj says in that crazy Punjabi lilt, and he pings another photo up on the screen for her to look at and nudges Big Mama to get her attention. 'Who's this then?'

Preity is standing helplessly behind them with her mouth hanging open. I make a face at her. Dhruv is determinedly lost in his phone. My mum avoids my gaze. Something is indeed very, very wrong with Big Mama. We can't pretend. Not anymore. There'll be no more arguments about medication or no medication, no disagreements about diagnosis, no more pretending she's having a phase and she'll be better soon. A big part of Big Mama is gone.

Pudding arrives, giant dollops of creamy aromatic rice. You've never seen so many calories on one plate, Biggy's plate, and she's laying into it like there's no tomorrow and she hasn't eaten for a week.

'Fruit pakora, anyone?'

But they all refuse. Except Biggy who nibbles on a banana dripping with syrup.

'What day is it, Big Mama?' I ask her.

'What day is it?' she says. 'Why do I need to know what day it is? I know what day it is. You tell me what day it is.' She looks at me over the laptop. Her eyes are full of fear and sadness and she slumps back in her chair like a sulky child.

So I tell her it's Sunday and I'm just teasing, but not that it's

Mother's Day because she's forgotten that already.

The tea arrives. A big cupful lands in front of her.

'I only want half a cup,' she says.

'Just drink what you want and leave the rest,' says my mum with a sigh of despair. She knows this won't work.

'But I only want half a cup,' repeats Biggy. Some things she knows for sure.

'Just drink it Mamaji and leave half.'

'It's wasteful to do that. I just want half a cup.'

So I call the waitress back and explain the problem and she looks at me like I'm the one who's 'pagal' and takes the cup away. Another arrives, two-thirds full. Biggy peers inside then visibly relaxes.

'She never drinks a whole cup,' says Anju. We all know this.

'I know,' says my mum. 'I told them. They didn't believe anyone would be that daft.'

'What colour do you want to wear to the wedding?' I ask Biggy. 'Anything you like. Purple with orange spots? Tiger print? Pale pink?'

She laughs. This is a game she likes. 'I think turquoise with yellow flowers, red stripes and little green stars.' And we all laugh, more from relief than anything.

Soon it's time to go.

'Look,' my mum says to Biggy. 'The kids are paying. Isn't that nice? It's their present to you. Isn't that lovely?'

But Biggy looks positively scared. I can see she doesn't know why she is getting a present.

'It's for Mother's Day ...' I tell her, '... instead of a present.

What do you give the person who has everything she needs? Their favourite food, that's what, and bring all the family to see her. It's our Mother's Day treat.'

She too looks relieved. 'I know it's Mother's Day,' she says with a little shake of her head. 'Of course I know it's Mother's Day. I was only kidding!'

That night I can't sleep. I miss my sister, Deepa. I feel guilty for pushing it, but I think part of me needed to know, needed confirmation. Like a diagnostic formulation. I call my mum and Anju. I don't want to bother them but I needed my mums. I put the phone down before they pick up and send them a text instead. It's somehow easier. 'What should we do?'

Anju phones.

'Don't worry, Beti,' she says. 'We need to be strong, my girl. She's just getting old.'

'But what the fuck was that?' I say. 'She forgot Billy Connolly! If she's forgotten Billy Connolly, what else has she forgotten?'

'How do you mean?' Anju says.

'I mean it's like a big bit of her has just been scrubbed out,' I say. 'Like it's just not there anymore. As if it's died or something.'

'What else doesn't she remember?' she said, then she answered herself. 'She didn't know half the family photos, or she got them all wrong. Come on, you're the doctor. You must know what to do.'

'Yeah but …' I don't know what to say. I'd know if she was a patient and I was her doctor, but she's my Gran. She's Big Mama. 'It's like she's fucking died,' I say. 'Like she's just an empty vessel.'

There's a pause.

'She's not dead, Pinky, and stop swearing. We need to be strong. Let's get her to the doctor and do some tests, yeah?'

I like tests – although, as a psychiatrist, I know there isn't a conclusive one. Not for this.

My mum phones.

'I'm going to take her to the doctor,' says mum. 'She might have a vitamin deficiency. I read something in the Reader's Digest. Or maybe she needs a holiday – that special trip to India.'

It makes me want to puke. She's got DEMENTIA. Please see it. I don't want to see it either. I don't want to be the one to say it out loud. I know what happens but I don't want to feel it. I take a deep breath.

'Mum, can we talk please – just you, me and Anju.'

'Why?" says Mum.

'Because we need to figure out what to do.'

'There's nothing to figure out,' she says.

Same old cycle. We've been here before, when Biggy first started forgetting things; walking on eggshells, making fancy plans. Me promising I'll visit, then burying my head on the sand. It's disgusting. Deepa, my sister does it. Like Anju. Effortless. But Deepa isn't here. I'm scared to visit alone. How ridiculous. You see, I don't know what to say when I get there. And she just sits there offering me food that she doesn't have.

'How are you?' she'll say.

'Fine.'

'Have you eaten?'

'Yes.'

'Do you want to eat something?'

30

'No, thanks.'

End of conversation.

She doesn't actually cook any more, but she's forgotten that.

'Ok,' says mum. 'Let's have a meeting.'

When someone's memory is slipping away, the whole family goes into denial. I avoided Big. I was frightened of her. She looked the same but she wasn't. She felt the same, but she wasn't. I could read it in a textbook, see it every day in my clinic, but I didn't want to see it at home: old age, forgetfulness, absent mindedness eating away at my Big Mama slowly – till she forgot how to make me laugh, till I forgot how to bring her out of it, till I lost the bits of her that made me. But the fight was just beginning.

Someone once said to me 'Stop being a psychiatrist and start being a Granddaughter.' But what if your Gran isn't there anymore? Who do you start loving then?

Chapter 2

Big Mama, Biggy, or Big, my Gran, is a bit on the wee side. She's only four foot ten inches tall but she's the 'biggest' character in our family and she was a giant in my life from very early on. She has principles that are hugely important to her and strict codes of behaviour for all sorts of occasions, even including the order you put your clothes on in the morning: always pants first. I still can't do it any other way. Some of these codes used to get right up my nose, but if I'm honest I got most of my own principles from her.

This chapter is about Biggy's life and beliefs. It'll give you an idea of who she used to be. Some of this I heard about from my mum and my Anju Masi, and some is just stuff she told me herself, like the stuff from way back before we were even twinkles in anyone's eyes.

Biggy was born in a remote village in India called Ramdass. She had four brothers and four sisters, so there were nine in the family in all, and she was number five, right in the middle. It was a very close-knit family with strong family values, like the older girls looking after the younger ones and everybody helping out. This is what she did most of her younger days. She did get some school education in India but most of the time she was helping her mum with the siblings and doing household chores. This is why she's so house-proud now.

Then, when she was sixteen, she got married and thought she was very modern because her own mum was married at only fourteen. According to Big Mama, when her own mum was getting married, she peed herself in the dholi, the bridal palanquin, something I used to find hilarious when I was a kid. I suppose I thought it was ridiculous – what a thing to do at the age of fourteen! But now I'm horrified. Poor girl. Biggy says her mum didn't know where she was going and didn't understand what was happening at all. She must have been terrified.

Like her mum, Biggy's marriage was arranged, as is traditional, but those two extra years made a big difference and her wedding went off without incident. Phew! She quickly came to love my Granddad and doted on him, doing everything she could for him. Later, when we all came along, we all loved him too and everyone called him Papa Ji. In Hindi, 'Ji' after a name is a sign of great affection.

Then she went to Kenya. Papa Ji was born in India but he went to Kenya when he was quite young. He was taken there by his brother to work but he came to home to India to get married and then he and Biggy went back to Kenya together. He had a newsagent business there, which is what he always did wherever he was. Selling newspapers and running a shop. Biggy stayed with him all that time only coming back to India to see her family every so often.

She had her children in Kenya, all four of them: a boy and then three girls. They stayed in Kenya for nearly twenty years. While they were there they lived in a joint family, with Papa Ji's brother's family. Papa Ji's brother's wife was not a well woman and had lots of pregnancies which ended in miscarriages until finally she had a daughter. But nine years later the wife died and big-hearted Big Mama brought up this daughter along with her own children.

Then Papa Ji and Big Mama decided to sell the business and move back to India. Everyone tried hard to settle in India but somehow it just didn't work out. Maybe it was too big a change, but after a bit of a struggle they finally upped sticks and went back to Kenya.

All this was very disruptive to the kids' education, of course. My mum had always harboured a yearning to become a doctor, but moving about between two continents and adjusting from Kenya to India and back again put paid to that. She did eventually make it as a nurse, and a very good one at that, but it was her oldest brother who was sent to Britain to study engineering.

He stayed with a friend of the family, so he was in safe hands. But it was another adjustment to another new country and culture. He was desperately homesick. He wanted to give up his education and come home. But he was the only son between the two joint families so he was the great hope, maybe the only hope. They needed him to complete his education. So instead of him going home to Kenya, the whole family moved to Britain to be with him. This is how much Big Mama and Papa Ji believed in education.

Papa Ji set up another newsagents and my uncle went on with his studies. While they were doing all that my Gran was also working. She was very, very hard-working and very determined, even though she never did paid work outside the house. First, of course, her house was always spotless. When my mum and my aunt came home from school the dinner was always on the table. She had a dog to look after too and she had the shop that Papa Ji ran. She would go with him in the morning and help set up the papers, then she'd come back and get the kids off to school. Afterwards she'd go back with Papa Ji's breakfast, then she'd come home again to make the lunch and do a bit of cleaning and housework. After that she'd bring Papa Ji's lunch up to the shop, take the dog out for a walk and then in the evening the kids would come home from school, all needing feeding. Once fed, she'd go back down to the shop in the evening and help Papa Ji close up. It was hard going.

But the family had only been in Britain a year when there was a terrible accident, so awful it's hard to imagine how anyone could recover from something like that.

My uncle was driving up the motorway going to work when he had a flat tyre. It was early December and very cold. A friend that he worked with saw him struggling to change the wheel and stopped and came back to help. They were both bent over the wheel when another car skidded on black ice and ran right into them. The friend was thrown over the barrier and was hit by a car coming the other way. He died instantly. But my uncle was dragged under the wheel for a bit until the car managed to stop. Horrible. The driver of the car that skidded phoned for an ambulance, but my uncle died before getting to the hospital.

Biggy and Papa Ji were at the shop when the police came to the house. My mum sent the police down there and went to fetch her sister from the Eye Infirmary where she was working. Once everyone was gathered they were given the news. But of course, Biggy didn't speak the language and was new to this country. What can it have been like, to lose a son? It hardly bears thinking about. Biggy and Papa Ji had each other to console, but my mum says they all made more fuss of Papa Ji because he was a man in a house with four women and not good at letting his feelings out. Biggy, everyone felt, would talk if she needed to. She just got on with it. She always just got on with it. She had three remaining children to look after. But the grief she must have felt!

I never remember Big Mama moaning or groaning when I was younger, or being nasty or bitchy about anyone. She was never angry. She knew she just had to pick herself up and keep going.

They were offered compensation for his loss but they said no amount of money could ever make up for him passing away and gave it all to charity – so modern, yet somehow so traditional and strong.

Biggy doesn't remember the anniversary any more. It's not that she wants to forget; only that she isn't remembering lots of things. We always used to make a point of going and sitting with her on the day. We never used to mention why we were there, but we were always there just in case. I remember her crying with me once and she gave me a photo of him to put in our house.

We don't celebrate twenty-firsts in our family because it seems disrespectful. My mum organised a special prayer ceremony for my oldest brother when he turned twenty-one, but the rest of us didn't bother. It just didn't seem right.

Before my uncle died he had two dogs. The first one was an

Alsatian by the name of Simba. He was very big, too big in fact for the family to look after because he was so strong. Nobody was very big, least of all Biggy, and walking this dog was a problem. Initially he went to be a guard dog in a friend's shop, staying in the shop overnight where there had been a few break-ins. It was a great relief to find somewhere for him to go. However, the next day the shop owner phoned to say that the dog had eaten all the chocolate, been sick everywhere and generally trashed the shop. A new home was found for him and a new dog for my uncle.

The second dog was beautiful, a sandy-coloured mix of Alsatian and Labrador and only six weeks old. This one was to be trained. My uncle sent off for a manual, but then died two days later.

Biggy kept that dog and cherished him. I desperately want to remember him but I just don't, even though I've got a photo of him. Apparently I tormented him, pulling his tail and his ears, although, in my defence, I was only a toddler at the time. I'm told he tolerated all my annoying behaviour without complaint. His name was Moti and Biggy trained Moti even though she couldn't read the manual. She cared for him and fussed over him. He understood Punjabi and Hindi very well and understood what he was meant to do most of the time, unlike the rest of us! He was sponged down with a hot damp towel every day and if he went out for a walk he wasn't allowed back in the house until she had wiped his paws clean with a wet cloth. She fed him a curries and chapattis and rice and yoghurt and, although he had Alsatian in him, he wasn't very big and he knew how much pull to give when Biggy was walking him: not much. He had his own special sofa in the kitchen and that's where he died many years later in his sleep.

As I was growing up, I didn't quite understand her strong principles and beliefs, but that was then. I was only wee. Now I think a lot of my own beliefs come directly from her. For instance, she's always had a deep empathy for all living beings including animals and I'm a great animal lover too, especially cats. She's a vegetarian, of course, and now so am I. As a child I didn't understand the strength of her convictions. Looking back, we did some terrible things. We once fed her pepperoni pizza and told her it was made from peppers. 'Mmm,' she said. 'Delicious!' I'm horrified now, not least because we kept up this charade for weeks, ordering her delicious pepperoni pizza every weekend. What a transgression of her most deeply held beliefs! Shocking!

She was also unwaveringly kind to everyone and always forgiving. Thankfully she never found out about the pepperoni! Biggy was a quiet presence behind us, living a simple life with strong principles, albeit hard to understand at times.

Big Mama's brain kept going and she kept going until the last of her Grand-children was in formal education and had gone to university. Even now, when we go and visit and she has company, she still talks about 'This is my Grandson. He's a lawyer. This is my Granddaughter. She's a doctor.' She supported us through all sorts of troubles and made sure we all passed our exams and got to university. All this, yet she never had more than a little schooling herself.

She used to say, 'When my family are older and settled and you've all got your own homes and you've all got your good jobs, my job will be done.' Interestingly she never used to say 'When you've all got married and have husbands or wives.' It was always 'When you can all stand on your own two feet, my job will be done.' And she went just after we did.

She's still there in body, of course. That's the thing. We keep talking about her as if she's dead. She's not dead. She's there. She's in front of us. We can see her. She's still going to be there for all the events and the weddings and the graduations and the awards ceremonies. She'll still be there, but really she's gone.

I wonder sometimes, did she keep holding on and did she keep her brain active so that she could pass on some of her wisdom before it was too late, just so that we could all get settled?

I'm in awe of the sacrifice she made of her own individuality, her own life and anything she might have wanted to do. Occasionally I do wish I could be more like that and have her patience – but I'm horrified too, and angry.

I also wonder whether, if she'd used her brain more, she wouldn't be in the position she's in now, if she'd only tried harder. If, when she came to this country she'd learned to speak English, maybe her brain wouldn't be dying now the way it is. My mum wouldn't be berating herself for not doing more to help her learn how to get on in Scotland, pushing her to learn to drive, getting her to speak the language. Now that she's in a nursing home she can't understand what people are saying to her and she can't communicate her needs to them, and she doesn't eat the food. This is awful for her. We're finding it pretty difficult too, with my endlessly-patient mum practically living with her to ensure she gets the care she needs.

On top of all that, I'm a doctor. I'm supposed to be more supportive, more sympathetic. I'm supposed to understand. I'm supposed to know what to do. Why do I have to be all emotional about this? But when I put a medical spin on it I worry that's all I will ever do. The voices in my head say 'I'm her Granddaughter, for God's sake. Why do I have to analyse everything? This woman needs me. This woman brought me up. This woman is a human being.' When I go and visit I shouldn't be looking at her medication or thinking about when she's getting agitated. I should be going and giving her a hug and just trying to settle her down, but I can't. I don't know which role I'm supposed to play in all of this. And I don't know how to make it better.

My mum suffers from this too, being a nurse. And Biggy knows. 'You have become cold,' she'll say to her. 'You've been treating these patients and you've just become cold-hearted in treating your own mother.' And then Mum comes and cries to me.

The professional stance that Big Mama helped us to have, the textbook education, certainly didn't prepare us for what was to come.

My dad used to say to me when I was growing up, 'Pinky, I want you to become a doctor so that when I get sick you can look after me.' I've carried that guilt around for years because I couldn't help him when he was sick and I wasn't even a doctor at that point. I'm a doctor now, a psychiatrist working with young people, but I'm in the same profession that cares for people with dementia. Yet I can't do anything to help my Gran.

I don't have all the magic answers, yet I get annoyed when

40

people don't ask me or listen to my viewpoint because, scientifically, I know what's correct. But emotionally it feels like I don't know who she is any more. Or I don't want to know.

And I'm scared too. I'm scared of what's going to happen next and I'm scared of not having her. And I'm scared because, while I want some of her wisdom, I'm also a modern woman with a successful career and a man whom I love and am about to marry. In a couple of years I'll be having kids of my own. And I won't be dependent on Stephen the way Big Mama was dependent on Papa Ji for everything, and neither will I be picking up after him all day long. Moti's old sofa in Biggy's kitchen is in better shape than the one in my living room, even though it's half as old. I worry about the sacrifice and the boundless patience and love that I'll need but I don't think I have.

Maybe my generation is more selfish than hers, but how could she accept so little from life and be satisfied just living through others? Maybe I'm jealous. I wish I knew.

It's funny how quickly a lifetime can flash before your eyes. People look at the elderly and see the wrinkles, but they often forget about the stories that lie behind them. The hopes and fears of the current generation were once the ideas of those who were young before them: same feelings, same trepidation, same hope. And people often forget where the wisdom has come from. The experiences people have lived through and the advice they could share. How must a person feel when these entwined emotions and experiences start to unravel, when you know you're getting old, when people see you but look through you, when your opinion doesn't matter? And how must that person feel when their inner voice starts to become more confused, when you stop asking yourself any questions, because you can't remember what you want to know?

Laxmi, Raj, Biggy and Deepa

Chapter 3

I'm three. I'm standing on the corner of our street with my mum and two suitcases waiting for a taxi. My dad has stopped shouting and gone inside, slamming the door behind him so hard that the whole world seems to shake. Mum fiddles about in her bag looking for money for the taxi. She has a tissue and is dabbing at her ear for some reason, then her eyes. Maybe she has a cold. She's trembling too.

A neighbour comes round the corner. Mum turns and looks the other way. The neighbour doesn't smile but passes us quickly. I watch him walking briskly up the street.

'We're going to see Big Mama and Papa Ji!' says Mum in a cheerful voice.

I grin all over my face in happy anticipation. It's tea-time on Saturday and I'm woozy from a nap, but the thought of Big Mama brings me to my senses. We're early. Usually we wait for Dad to leave for the pub before we go to Big Mama and Papa Ji. Usually we get the bus, but then we don't usually have two suitcases.

'Are we staying the night?' I ask.

'Yes, Pinky Ji. We're staying the night, maybe a couple of nights, who knows?'

Delight makes me jump from foot to foot.

The taxi arrives. We climb in and Mum puts an arm round me and pulls me in close, where I like to be. The taxi sways round corners, shops and lights flit past the window and suddenly we are there. I get out first and bounce across the pavement to the close door. I know the button but I'm too little to reach it without being lifted.

'Mum!' I stretch up to it anyway, hoping I've grown. She struggles out of the taxi, pays the driver and lumbers over to join me. 'I want to do the button. Can I do the button? Up! I want up!' But she presses it quickly and leans in to listen to the intercom. She takes my hand and I feel hers shake.

The buzzer goes and she pushes the door and holds it open so I can pass through. I hear her bringing the suitcases in behind her as I rush up the stairs shouting.

'Biggy! Big Mama! Biggy! It's me! It's Pinky!'

It's two big flights and by the time I'm on the top step my mum is almost up behind me. Big Mama is standing in the doorway in her pinny, pulling off pink rubber gloves. She beams down at me and I crash into her arms and hold on tight. She and Mum are talking but all I can think about is the big fat chips we'll be having later and the cornflakes with extra sugar in the morning. I let go of Biggy and rush through to the front room where Papa Ji is reading his paper.

'Hello, young lady,' he says, closing his paper and turning with a ready smile. 'And what brings you here today?'

'Daddy was shouting again,' I say.

'Oh dear,' he says with a sigh. He glances at the door then reaches out and pushes it shut. 'What about a game of cards? Chakri, that's my favourite.'

Of course, Daddy was doing more than shouting, but my

mum and Big Mama did a good job of keeping me from the truth for as long as possible. Swift exits from our house and sudden arrivals at Biggy's were a normal part of life for me. They meant being fussed over and cuddled and watching TV and sleeping tucked up with Mum.

Later that night I'm dozing off, this time squeezed in between Mum and Big Mama on the sofa, when suddenly I'm awake again. Mum rushes to the window. I can hear shouting in the street, all the way up those two big flights. It sounds like my dad but how could that be? Big Mama lifts me and I decide it's a bad dream and she takes me through and slides me into a cosy warm bed with a hot water bottle and a teddy.

Fast-forward through a couple of years of this to-ing and fro-ing, with Biggy picked me up from nursery and school most days while my parents both worked. I often had her completely to myself and we did the things little girls do with their Grans like going to all the local shops for bits and pieces, me watching Biggy choose her apples carefully then haggle the greengrocer down. Sometimes she took me fabric shopping – Biggy made all her own clothes. I loved touching all the colourful rolls and pulling them out so the silk would unfold as was I wrapped up inside it. Biggy taught me to knit and she let me sit in the kitchen corner while she cooked the most amazing things. We were companions, accomplices, playmates and she was a goddess of calm and comfort.

Meanwhile my mother stoically returned to her marital home, taking me with her, continuing to try and make it work. That included the arrival of Deepa and Raj, so of course having Big

46

Mama all to myself soon came to an end.

Here I have to tell you: my mum is one of the strongest women you will ever meet. She's also one of the most, stubborn, obstinate and defensive, particularly when emotional situations occur. She's tried to be a nurse. She's tried to be a daughter. She's always wanted to be a son to my Grandparents because they lost their own son at an early age, but she couldn't do that because of the abusive relationship.

'That's life,' she says to me now. 'I counsel myself. I just talk to myself any time my thoughts are getting really bad, and I say to myself *It'll be ok and we can do this*.' It doesn't mean she always practices what she preaches but her inner strength and courage have been a building block for this whole family. Where did this strength and that courage come from? I can see now it came from my Gran.

You see, Biggy was like a huge force at that time, a giant. Even though we always went back to my dad, the one thing my mum never gave up on was Biggy.

My dad used to say my Gran and Granddad were bastards. He would say it in Punjabi so it always sounded worse. Really dirty. He would say that they were low-lifes, claiming social security and sitting around doing nothing. I had no idea what social security was but it didn't sound bad. He said they weren't my real family. He used to pull the phone out of the socket and smash it up so that we couldn't contact them. He even had BT install a block for their number and for Anju Masi's number too. We had to walk to a phone box in the rain to call them.

'She's my mum,' is what my mum used to say. End of story.

Except it wasn't. My dad decided to ban all visits to Big Mama and Papa Ji completely. Except he couldn't. Luckily he was fairly regular in his own indulgent habits. The sudden exits and arrivals continued and the sneaking about began.

I wonder how many people need to sneak off to see their Grandparents. I wonder how many families need to sneak anywhere. We were masters of sneaking from a very young age. I quickly learned the difference between a bad lie and a lie that would stop a fight occurring; the art of diplomacy and keeping the peace. As I became older a mean streak developed and I could manipulate a fight by lighting the match and watching the house burn. But that was later.

When I was seven I remember following after my dad as he wandered off to the pub, usual for him on a Saturday afternoon.

'Quiet, kids, and walk sensibly. No sudden movements,' said Mum. Raj was only a baby being carried and Deepa was four. It can't have been easy. Dad turned and gazed back up the road. I was sure we'd been seen. We all froze like statues, though not very good ones, but then Dad carried on walking with that swagger of his and we all breathed sighs of relief. Deepa and I giggled nervously. At the bus stop we chased each other round the shelter until the bus came. Mum cooed at Raj who was teething and wriggly and jigged him up and down, and she paced anxiously up and down the shelter until the bus finally arrived.

Arriving at Biggy's, Deepa and I raced for the buzzer, but being bigger I always got there first. This time I lifted her up to press it herself.

Biggy's house was warm. We ordered pizza, she made those

48

chips I always loved and we watched a Bollywood film. She fed me peanut butter straight from the jar and we watched Eastenders which was a favourite of hers. I thought it was boring then, but now it's the other way round.

'Bad man, bad man,' said Biggy, about Dirty Den. Strangely she never said that about my dad. Somehow she always forgave Dad through it all. It seems strange to me. Even recently as her demented self, in a lucid moment she said 'Just let him go. Just let him go away. Be at peace and remember that your forgiveness is important for his soul. Yes, he did bad things but we don't know what demons he was fighting and what hurt he had to suffer.'

I didn't understand much then because I was too busy being seven and because Biggy made sure I didn't know.

Biggy sat me on her knee and repeated the same mantra like she always did: 'Be good to your parents, listen to your parents and work hard. May God Grant you health, wealth and happiness. You will study hard and have a family of your own one day. Family is the most important thing, your mum and your dad.' Then she tickled me and chased me round the house.

I hung on to her every word and tried really hard to see this perfect family through her eyes. I guess I learned to love the monster that was my father because she taught me to.

In the evening, when it was time to go, we all got kisses and hugs before going back down the two flights of stairs and out into the street to the bus stop. As we neared home and Raj was asleep and Deepa dozing off, Mum and I peered out at my dad's pub and the streets between it and home.

'Wake up, Deepa,' she said. 'It's time to get off. Pinky, take her hand. Quickly now, before he beats us home.'

The bus shuddered to a halt and we thanked the driver and got off. Ironically Deepa and I hate buses now. I won't travel on them. I call them 'bastard buses' even to this day. Maybe people think I'm a snob but I hate the shuddering and I hate the smell. It reminds me of the shit we went through. Shit like that very day. Behind us, away off in the distance, wandering along with two other men, I saw my dad!

'Mum,' I said, tugging at her sleeve. 'Mum! He's there, look.'

She stopped a moment and took my hand, then peered back and drew breath. Again her hand trembled in mine. There was a pause.

'Ok, you two, run,' she said. 'Deepa you go with Pinky. Run ahead and see who can get home first. I'll follow. Last one home's a tattie sprout.'

'What's a tattie sprout?' I said as I started off.

'Go, Pinky!'

So we raced each other, playing my mum's game.

'Come on, Dippy! Bet you can't beat me.' Of course she couldn't, but I let her win anyway, at least until the gate, then I steamed on past her to the front door and leant on the bell as if there was somebody home. As soon as my mum arrived with Raj we ran in.

'Ok, night-suits on then back down to the living room as quick as you can, TV on and throw some toys around so he won't know.'

Mum went into the kitchen to heat milk for hot chocolate. Deepa and I ran to our room and brought our night clothes and bedtime toys down to the living room and clicked the telly on, tossing our clothes around the room as we took them off. Then on with the jammies and the slippers, Barbie flung in one corner, Ken in the other, Eeyore over the back of the sofa. On TV, one of those eighties cop shows flickered across the screen. The screech of a car-chase ended in a giant crash and a stunned silence. Just then, Dad's key clicked in the lock and we leapt onto the couch and hugged each other tight.

Raj was with Mum in the kitchen. He started to cry.

'What are you doing out of bed at this time?' said Dad, incredulous. He clocked the telly. 'And watching this shite? What's going on? Get up there to bed now and take all this rubbish with you.' He picked up Eeyore and we cowered as it arced across the room and bounced off the window. We hadn't even closed the curtains. 'Now!' he roared. 'Bed!' he bellowed. 'Rita!' he screamed.

We leapt off the sofa and ran to the door.

'Come back here!' he yelled. 'You can take this rubbish with you.' He kicked my jumper into the air and oddly I caught it. 'Get a move on! Now!'

Deepa started to cry. She stood with the dress she'd had on twisted in her little hands, frozen to the spot. I quickly picked up the rest of her clothes and mine and dragged her out of the room and upstairs to bed. I could hear him kicking our toys out of his way behind us in the front room. The TV went silent then he thundered down the hall.

'Rita!' he shouted.

Raj wailed in the kitchen.

The row began.

'Why are these kids not in bed?'

Deepa and I both got into my bed together and hid under the covers.

Raj cried out. We couldn't hear Mum, only Dad yelling. All we could do was wait.

Miraculously Deepa fell asleep soon after and maybe I did too because the next thing I knew, someone was creeping into the room and peering over us. I looked up and Mum was there, still cradling Raj in her arms.

'Where's Deepa?' she whispered.

I pulled back the cover to reveal the top of Deepa's head.

'Ooh,' she mouthed. Then she smiled. 'He didn't guess,' she whispered, 'and he's fast asleep already.' She put Raj into his cot then lifted Deepa out and laid her safely in her own bed. Then she came back and pulled the covers back up snug around my neck and kissed me goodnight.

This became the pattern of our sneaking, only we got better at it so we wouldn't get caught, always setting things up beforehand to look like we'd been there all evening. Sometimes there was trouble anyway and we'd do our sharp exit, arriving at Biggy's with suitcases, sometimes staying a night, sometimes longer. On those occasions he sometimes followed and stood over the road shouting up at the window or came up to the door and hammered on it with his fists. He really hated Biggy and Papa Ji.

'One day you'll realise who your real family are!' he'd shout, illogically.

He used to say he'd dance on their graves when Big Mama

52

and Papa Ji died. Big Mama would take me into the kitchen so I couldn't hear. She never asked questions, just put the saucepan on to make tea (she had no kettle) and let us watch Bollywood films. She'd make chapattis, break them up and coat them with sugar. Yum! She knew how to distract and comfort us.

Finally, it got too much. He used to hit my mum so badly that Mum couldn't bear it any longer and tried to take her own life. Somehow Biggy knew, I don't know how, and dialled 999. An ambulance turned up at our house and took my mum away. We were sent to our room and weren't allowed to see what was going on. I was only ten. We stayed up there the rest of the evening without any dinner though we could hear him downstairs watching TV. The next day Biggy turned up in a taxi and took us to stay with her. He let her. She was always my saviour, my protector, never letting me down.

A few days later Biggy took me to the hospital to see my mum. I remember walking down the corridor holding her hand.

'Don't cry, Pinky,' said Big Mama. 'Your mum will be upset. We have to be happy for her.'

So I tried. I smiled for Biggy because she said it was right and Biggy was always right. I found out later that Biggy made my mum promise that she would never do that again. My mum has said the same thing to me when I've been distressed about the things life's thrown my way. She says a mother would give her own life before she'd let her kids feel even the pain of a scratch.

But I needed Biggy. I was lost without her. I remember her and Papa Ji going to India for three weeks. I refused to leave their house because I was so scared without them. They came back

53

with so many presents they must have paid a fortune in excess baggage. One of the things Biggy brought me was a holy book – the Bhagavad Gita. It was in English too and I read it many times. I still find peace from it. I find peace from it because I can hear her voice through it, not because I'm religious.

We always went back to my dad eventually – even after Mum tried to take her life again, even though sometimes we stayed away so long we had to go into a refuge. When I was nine we stayed in one but went back home because my mum thought I wanted to. Maybe I didn't realise how bad it was for her. Maybe I was just sick of refuge life: no phone, no friends round for tea, no playing outside in case we were seen. Maybe I said I wanted to go because I thought it was what she wanted. I don't know. I was too young to make that kind of decision anyway. It should never have been up to me.

Back home things went from bad to worse to absolutely diabolical. As the years passed I became a stroppy teenager with bells on. I'd had enough. I'd seen enough and I wasn't putting up with it any more. My mum says now that if we hadn't gone back to the refuge, I'd have killed my dad or he'd have killed me. It's weird that I now work with kids who've done things like killing one of their parents.

Anyway, back to the refuge we went and this time we stayed. There was no way I was going home.

Kids grow up in fairy tales, once-upon- a-times and happily-ever- afters. Very few kids actually go through reality unscathed. But what every kid needs is a stable figure, a sounding board, a protecting influence. As a child you think time is infinite and that everything lasts forever. You take that for granted and live without care. But the hand that once held your small hand will ultimately weaken and wither and it's up to you to grab onto that ageing limb and hold on tight.

But the demented person, my Biggy, is being pulled into her own reality; she isn't there anymore to see I have survived, that I am blooming and flourishing. And it feels so empty without her. What would she have said if she could have seen the future? What would she think if she could remember the past? What would I have felt like if I'd survived unscathed?

Chapter 4

I've always thought that the more you tell someone not to do something, the more they'll want to do it. But who stops a child seeing their Grandparents? Did I love going to see Biggy because it felt naughty and adventurous? Did I want to go and see her because I've always been a bit defiant? Either was I have my dad to thank. Paradoxically, through his determination to stop us forming a bond with Big Mama and Papa Ji, he shone a light on the strength there was within that family. He exposed the heart of forgiveness, of calm, and of thought. He showed me the power of love and family unity. I know who my real family are. I've always known. My mum fought for that and my Grandparents stood by us, even when I was being difficult and obstinate.

I used to love going round to Biggy for a feed. Not that I was particularly keen on revolting things like aubergine or egg curry that she made sometimes. I think she knew something was wrong when I actually refused to eat, so I haven't seen egg curry on a plate since I was about ten. She was a pretty skilled lady, making her own ice cream, cultured yoghurt, ghee, bread, biscuits and of course homemade chips! I can't recall how many potatoes I would have in the one sitting (I dread to think) but she just kept frying. It must have taken her the whole day on Saturdays, peeling and cutting up potatoes with her arthritic hands, salting them a wee bit with a little paprika and then frying them as we all sat at the table in anticipation. I used to drown mine in vinegar and smother them with salad cream. Biggy used to warn me not to drink the vinegar, saying I would end up with an ulcer. I did and I have!

I went vegan in my teens but didn't realise salad cream had egg in it. I was hardly eating anything at that time and I remember overhearing Biggy talking to my mum about salad cream having eggs in it. Maybe she'd read the label.

'It's ok,' she said to my mum. 'Let her find out about the eggs and make her own decision whether she wants to eat salad cream.'

We also had this thing where Hindus shouldn't eat eggs on a Tuesday. My viewpoint on this is that it's just plain weird. I remember asking Big to explain it when I was about eight. I can't remember what explanation she gave, but I know that I've never seen the point of such ritualistic behaviour and that she respected my opinion. She never shouted at me for asking questions and did not profess to have all the answers either. What tended to antagonise me when I was teenager was this apparent defaulting to God when an answer wasn't readily available. But maybe that's the power of faith.

I was rather less respectful of her beliefs. This was the time of the pepperoni incident when we fed her pepperoni pizza and told her it was made from peppers. And we didn't leave it as a one-off. It happened over several weeks. It was a terrible way to repay her kindness.

But going round to see the Grandparents wasn't just about Biggy. In some ways she was the background person, hoovering, wiping down the sofas, climbing on chairs to dust shelves and lampshades, cleaning and cooking in the kitchen. We were usually more taken with Papa Ji and usually sat on his knee (even when I was taller than him and weighed more than he did). I used to copy the way he sat with one leg crossed over the other, in fact I still sit like that most of the time. He liked to use a cup and saucer for his tea, not a mug. He would tip the tea into the saucer and slurp it up from there. I still do this sometimes in secret! Deepa and I used to play like this, copying him. We would watch Blind Date together and the Generation Game and Biggy used to sit on the floor and knit. It was about this time she did her Billy Connolly thing for the first time.

This is how it went. We're all sitting round laughing our heads off at Billy Connolly on the telly and Biggy's sitting, clickety-click, knitting some crazy jumper or hat when suddenly she stops, looks up and says:

'Why are you laughing at this Billy Connolly? All he ever says is "Bloody fucking. Bloody fucking."'

And we all fell about laughing even more, and then we're all going "Bloody fucking. Bloody fucking" just like her in her crazy Indian accent. "Bloody fucking. Bloody fucking!" Biggy joined in of course and it became her party piece which, until that Mother's Day meal, she did right on cue, every time. Shocking.

Going to Biggy's also meant we got to see my Aunt Anju, that's Anju Masi: Masi means aunt. She was, and still is, the coolest woman in town: glamorous, trendy, free and oh so modern. She was a dance teacher and would make up routines in Biggy's house. My dad used to say only prostitutes danced. So I asked him what a prostitute was and he swore at me.

Anju Masi introduced us to Chinese take-aways and she was the person who gave me my first manicure. My dad oscillated between sucking up to her and bitching about her. I used to have a picture of her on my bedroom wall. I didn't want to be a celebrity; I wanted to be Anju Masi. One day I came home from school and the picture had been torn up and scattered all over my bed. I found another picture to replace it, but that disappeared too. So I learnt to keep the pictures hidden so they were safe. Anju Masi sometimes went on holiday (we didn't do holidays – we were Indian apparently) and she would always bring me back lots of presents.

Biggy's house looked onto Argyle Street, one of the main roads from the centre of Glasgow out to the West End. It always felt like the biggest, busiest, most dangerous road in the world. I still have that feeling when I cross it today. Their second floor flat was on a corner and I would sometimes sit at the window just looking out over the world. I could see Yorkhill children's hospital with its pink windows from her living room.

'Do you think you might work there one day?' Biggy said to me. She knew. I did. I do. I work there often. It was as if she could see into the future.

We used to hear the orange walks too from up there and I loved watching them marching through the city centre. We got a great view. We were never taught that it wasn't 'our thing' or that we shouldn't be watching. Biggy even took me down when they were passing once, so we could clap along to the music.

Biggy and Papa Ji's house had the tiniest bathroom you ever saw and it had a little window which opened onto the close. The window always reminded me of a window in a jail, although it didn't feel that way. I used to go into the bathroom, sit on the toilet and sing away or talk to myself. I didn't make the connection that everyone could hear me in the close until I climbed up on the toilet seat one day and peered out and there were Biggy and my mum giggling down below.

They never told me to keep quiet, never stopped me expressing myself even though their own way was to say little and shy away from the limelight.

Biggy never dressed in trousers or dresses. Instead she always wore brightly coloured Punjabi suits, or saris for special occasions. And she always wore a matching cardigan and sensible shoes. She never ever wore trainers with her outfits: that would have been a total cringe! I remember getting a long maroon dress from Quiz for my twelfth birthday. I put her in it and took a picture. She looked like a little doll. I've looked for that photo long and hard but I just can't find it. What a gem that would be!

Biggy also had a collection of lipsticks all lined up on her dresser. They were mainly testers from my Aunt Anju's pharmacy. They were always plastic and had that coloured bit shaped like a lipstick on the top. But Big Mama didn't really have lips. I'm sure she did have them once, but I used to wonder where she used to put the lipstick!

I stole a lipstick once. I put it down my pants. I had a skirt on and the lipstick fell out in the living room. My mum was so angry, so ashamed. But Biggy was unruffled. She said there was no need to steal in her house. If I asked her she would give me anything I wanted – if she could. She used to wear a silver Om pendant on a chain. She gave it to me and told me it would keep me safe. I still treasure it.

Biggy's house was also the setting for some very serious events. My dad would often force himself in and start a fight, begging for us to come back. I remember making up a contract for him in Biggy's kitchen. I coloured it in and everything and asked my dad to sign it. It was a promise that he wouldn't hit my mum anymore. He signed it and promised. The promise lasted two days.

During those days he suggested we buy the big flat above Biggy's so we could be close to her. He even took me round to view it, and Deepa and I picked out our rooms. We were so excited. He didn't mean it though and I cried for days.

Biggy had a painting in her living room of two zebras on a background of gold. Anju Masi brought it back from Kenya for her. I used to stare at the zebra's stripes until my eyes went funny. I didn't have to hear what was going on. It didn't always work.

One afternoon I was staring out the window when I realised the house had gone very quiet. I crept out to the hall and heard people whispering in the kitchen. The door was open just enough for me to see that Mum, Big Mama and Anju Masi were doing something round the kitchen table. There was a flash of something yellow and I suddenly saw it was the Tweety Pie nightdress that I had saved up for ages to buy my mum. It had been cut up.

'Do you think she'll notice?' said my Mum. 'Look, I tried to sew it back up but it's a bit bumfled here and under the arm. It's the best I could do.'

'I'll have a go with it,' said Big Mama. 'You go and have a lie down. I'll bring you hot milk when you wake up.'

'The man's a monster,' said Aunt Anju. 'And Pinky's not stupid.'

I heard my mum cry.

'It's only a night-dress,' offered Anju.

'It's not just a night-dress,' whispered my mum. 'It'll be me next. It'll be me he chops into pieces.'

I held on to my gasp. No-one spoke but the rustle of chiffon told me there were hugs and kisses and more tears.

'He's completely out of control,' my mum went on. 'I don't know what to do. There isn't room for us here.'

'You can always stay here, my darling,' said Biggy. 'The bed is there for you and the kids. Always there.'

'But there are four of us and they're not little any more. Pinky is too old. She needs a room, Raj is a boy. He can't be sleeping with his sisters at his age. No. But we can't go back. We can't.'

I sneaked back along the hall to the window and gazed out at all the cars and buses rumbling and grumbling along the street and all the people crossing between them and not seeming worried about anything at all. I didn't want to leave Biggy's, but Mum was right, there wasn't room. So we went back to the refuge.

That's where we were, in a refuge, when my standard grade results were due out. We weren't allowed to disclose our address so we arranged to have the certificate delivered to Big Mama's house. Deepa was so excited. We went to Biggy's the afternoon before and planned to stay up all night and watch films. I lasted (as I usually did) till ten o'clock. Deepa managed to stay up all night and in the morning everyone was waiting in the hall for the envelope to fall through the door.

At last it came. We all rushed at it at once. Deepa got there first and handed it straight to me.

'Go on then!' she said, jumping around the hall like a lunatic. 'Open it! Open it! What does it say? What did you get? Let's see.'

'Out of my way!' I shouted. 'You're crowding me! I can't see it. Let me get to the window. Give me space.'

I don't know what I expected but I wanted to read it by myself. I didn't want Deepa or Biggy or anybody else leaning over my shoulder. It was mine and it was too important. They let me through to the window, following me like the tail of the dragon. They all held their breath.

I put my back to the window and opened the envelope.

'What does it say?' said Deepa.

'Leave me alone!' I shouted.

Deepa flumped down on the sofa with her arms crossed.

'Pinky Ji …' said my mum. But she waited.

The certificate was simple. It was easy to read. I drew a huge lungful of air.

'I got all ones,' I said, in disbelief.

Deepa was back off the sofa, jumping and whooping. My mum hugged me. Biggy hugged me. Then she took the certificate, which she wouldn't have been able to read, and kissed it.

I waited until she was finished. I waited until they'd all finished then I took the certificate and went back to the refuge for some peace. I was grateful for their excitement, for their pleasure at my success, but I was fifteen and needed to be on my own.

I still dream about Big Mama's house in Argyle Street. For years most of my dreams seemed to happen there. Good dreams and bad dreams, all sorts of dreams, but always the one venue. It doesn't happen so frequently now. I heard the building was going to be demolished, but when I drove past recently there was construction work going on. The next time there were new windows. Every time I pass I look up in case there's a 'For Sale' sign. Maybe I could buy it. And take Biggy back to see if she remembers feeding the pigeons out of the little window at the back.

Families, you can't pick them, but what if you could? Would you choose the one you have? Would a different one have made you any better or any worse? Would they have picked you? Looking in on other people's lives, you could become disillusioned. Society makes judgments on everything, but nobody knows the pain of growing up too quickly or growing old too fast. Time stops for no one but its relevance changes for each of us. Those with dementia have no concept of time, and those watching the sufferer often find it stands still. As a child, time flies. As a child in a refuge, it seemed obscure. But time is a funny thing, no matter what age you are.

Memories are precious. They are the foundation of who we are. Without them, are we nothing?

Chapter 5

My dad came to Biggy's to tell me. I didn't believe him at first. He got heartburn a lot, which isn't surprising considering how much he drank, but he always thought it was something more serious, like a heart attack. So I thought he was just being a drama queen as usual.

'I went for this scan,' he said. 'They told me it's cancer.' He pulled at his collar. 'Cancer of the oesophagus.'

'The what?' I said. I remember exactly where I was too, on the blue leather sofa in Biggy's, the one she used to clean all the time.

'The gullet,' he said, 'cancer of the gullet.' He felt with his hand round his neck, one side and then the other.

'Yeah, right,' I said. 'No doubt you've got a brain tumour too.' I didn't believe a word of it.

'I'm serious, Laxmi,' he said. 'This is for real. You shouldn't joke about this kind of stuff.' Laxmi is my official name, his mum's name which he insisted on my being called.

'You've always got something wrong with you,' I said. 'This is just a load of fucking codswallop really, isn't it? And you're having another heart attack and another scan. We're not coming back, you know. Your little ploy is not going to work. You made your bed, so you can lie in it.'

We were in the refuge again at this point and there was no way I was going back. My mum and I had been fairly agreed on this when we'd left a few weeks before.

'Either you're going to kill him and end up in prison or it'll be him killing you,' she said at the time, 'but something's going to happen.'

I was fifteen going on sixteen when we went to the refuge the second time, and a total teenager. I was not putting up with this shit all over again. But as the truth dawned on me, that my dad's illness was genuine this time, I realised things might have to change.

But history repeated itself.

'Do you want to go back?' my mum asked. 'He is your dad and he's only got two years to live.'

'Not on your nelly!' I said. 'You're not putting this back on me for the second time. And what about my exams anyway?'

My Highers were coming up the next year, the school leaving exams in Scotland. Everything rested on them, the whole of my life, my future, my career, my independence. I was adamant. So we stayed in the refuge, even though the cancer was genuine.

A crowd of my dad's nephews appeared from India, sent by my uncles, his brothers. They were young men of about twenty and only stayed a couple of weeks. Some of them accused me of being callous and shrewd, as if there was some gain for me in all this. They didn't know how bad he had been to my mum.

Dad went for chemotherapy at the Western Infirmary and sometimes I'd go with him. He was still my dad, after all and I didn't want him to go through this entirely alone. He was quite pathetic though. I've always thought hospitals have a particular smell, the smell of people decaying. My dad had that smell, even though he was a clean person. I can't ever remember him smelling really strongly of alcohol or fags or whatever, but he had this horrible decaying smell. Despite this, I used to go down to visit him during my school lunch break. Sometimes, if he was sleeping, he didn't even know I was there. I'd go back to the school and tell people I was having a walk or up in the chemistry lab or some excuse. I'd then resume normal activity.

For someone who liked inflicting hurt on other people, he made a terrible patient. He was a cry baby, even at the littlest things, even before the cancer. I remember my mum and he were having a fight one time and she shut the door on his arm and leg. He sat upstairs on my bed for hours wailing in agony. I gave him my snoopy teddy because I didn't know what else to do.

'You need to phone the doctor,' he said. 'You need to phone the ambulance. She's killed me!'

And I thought, 'For God's sake, you beat women, but you can't take it yourself.'

But undoubtedly, as he was dying, he suffered terrible pain, and he didn't handle it with any decorum.

He wasn't supposed to know where the refuge was. There were very strict rules, for obvious reasons; we weren't even allowed friends up or phones. Even so, it was on a big busy main road and not particularly well hidden. Eventually, of course, he found out where it was, but he wasn't allowed in.

He used to come and pick me up outside the refuge in his BMW and I'd go to the radiotherapy with him at the Beatson. I missed him once by accident and walked to the hospital myself. He looked so happy to see me. It hit me then that this was serious. He started losing loads of weight too and for a while I thought he was looking pretty good. But on Christmas Eve, when my sister and I went round to see him, the house looked bare and cold and far too big. He was sleeping in the living room on the floor next to the fire. It was a pathetic sight.

But he still hadn't changed. Once, while he was there having his chemo, I wound up in hospital myself with abdominal pain. By some weird coincidence I was put in the ward underneath his. They opened me up to have a look and, finding nothing, stitched me up again and put me to bed to recover. After the anaesthetic had worn off, my mum and Anju Masi came to visit.

'I knew there was something wrong,' said my mum, handing me a pair of tweezers. 'Because of your eyebrows. They're completely wrecked.' I was very particular about my eyebrows and used to tweeze them constantly.

My dad appeared from upstairs complete with his drip stand and those nephews of his, all the way from India. He then decided to have a fight with my mum. I mean, why not? There clearly wasn't enough stress going round. He did his usual thing of going right up close to her and shouting.

'This is all your fault,' he shrieked. 'You see what a useless mother you are? Letting my daughter wind up in hospital! Look at the state of her. You're not feeding her right.' A huge row erupted and all the time my mum's trying to calm him down.

'Right, that's enough,' she said, backing away. 'Not in the hospital.'

And I'm thinking 'Mum's fault? I see, so this is nothing to do with my having a lifetime of stress and not knowing whether we're all coming or going and the fact we don't have a home and I've got Higher exams coming up?'

By the time I'd thought all that, she was on the other side of the bed and he, despite being as ill as he was and trailing a drip stand, had lunged over the top of me and gone for her. Luckily everyone else managed to stop him and the ward staff came in and took him back upstairs. I think that's the last time he tried it.

He also gave me a mobile and used to ring every morning just to see how I was. I never wanted to speak to him actually. In fact this was an old ritual even when we were in the house. He'd be in his shop from very early in the morning and we'd be at home getting ready for school.

'How are you?' he'd say.

'I'm fine,' I'd say.

'What are you thinking?'

And what I'd really be thinking, but not saying of course, was, 'I don't know. Shut up. What if I don't want to tell you what I'm thinking? If I told you the truth you'd shout at me.'

He carried this on when we were in the refuge and right through his illness. It was actually the last thing I wanted.

He had a 'Hickman line' which was a tube which stuck out of his neck so they could give him his drugs directly into a central vein. Sometimes he'd turn up at my school with it just sticking out of his neck. I supposed he must have arranged to come because you're not meant to leave the hospital when you have one of these. One time when he was in for chemo he decided he wanted to feed the birds so he 'escaped' from hospital and went to Kelvingrove Park nearby. The police were called and then me.

He still had his line protruding from his neck and a loaf of bread in his hand. He thought the whole thing was hilarious.

I never really paid much attention to how everyone else was during this time. I was too self-absorbed, too busy being a stroppy teenager. I also wasn't privy to all the stuff that went on, glad sometimes to be treated as a child for once, but I know he went up to the pharmacy Anju Masi and Yogi Uncle had and had words with them. And I know he spoke to my Gran and Granddad. My mum says she made her peace with him before he died. Big Mama and Papa Ji visited him in the hospice and Biggy used to take him baby food to eat when his swallowing was bad. She'd feed it to him with a spoon. This is the Mother he could have had if he'd just had the sense, but he only realised it as he lay there dying in that hospice. Big Mama prayed for him. She forgave him. She loved him just like she loved everyone.

Whatever his journey was in those months, I think he tried to make his peace and to get some answers from all the people who were supposed to be his family and who didn't abandon him even at the end.

He didn't last two years but died only fourteen months after his diagnosis. The hospice had my mobile number as a contact because we weren't allowed a phone in the refuge. One of the sisters called the night before he died and said he had requested no visitors but that he was fine. At nine in the morning she called again to say he wanted to see us. I remember specially asking if he was ok. She wouldn't tell me. The funny thing was, a while before, Biggy had given me a red thread from the temple. It's supposed to be sacred. She had told me to tie one half on my dad

70

and keep the other half on my own wrist. My half broke off that morning, so I kind of knew. I still have that thread, my half.

Mum was working night shifts as a care assistant in a nursing home, minimum wages and long hours. She hadn't done her 'return to practice' qualification yet. She'd been out of nursing for thirty years and had to get this qualification, almost a re-qualification, to be able to practice as a nurse again, which would make her independent. It was the weekend and she had just come off night shift. My brother Raj and sister Deepa were still sleeping, so my mum and I drove straight down to Queen Margaret's hospice in Clydebank, about twenty minutes away, Bollywood music blaring.

I was wearing an orange 'Little Miss Naughty' top and black jeans with my midriff showing. It was ten days before the first of my Highers and I had been studying logarithms for my Maths exam. I had a strict timetable. When we got there we were ushered into this stupid room with stupid pink paint. Everything seemed to take forever. My mum went out and was gone for ages.

We had missed him by ten minutes.

She asked me if I wanted to go in and see him. So I did. Mum lifted the covers and I looked.

'Look how swollen he is,' she said.

I could have punched her. I didn't know what to say. She left me alone for a bit and I just felt dead inside. I can't really remember going back to tell my siblings and I don't remember how we got back to Big Mama's house, just that suddenly we were there, as if by magic. I retreated to Big Mama's bedroom with my cassette player and just played my music. Anju Masi arrived and said she thought I might need a sedative, but Biggy said just to leave things.

Nobody could come up for mourning at our house because it was a refuge, that shameful place where nobody was supposed to know you existed. So everyone bundled up to her house. The laying out was at Big Mama's too. She lived just round the corner from the refuge. Most of the people who came to the laying out never knew me or my dad. That's certainly what it felt like at the time. I recognised a few faces, and the priest that didn't like me. I was given a long top that belonged to Biggy because you can't fucking show off your midriff when your dad has just died.

They did this thing call 'absose' where people show up and stare at you and you have to be a living ornament for them and cry on cue. I was slightly detached during this. My impression from Eastenders was that, when someone died, you went to the pub, or you were left alone. I didn't get to do either. I had to pray, watch others pray, mix with folk who all knew my dad was a bastard but came to have a nosy. They were acting like they cared but inside I thought they were all glad he had gone. I was selfish during that absose. I don't remember comforting my siblings or my mum. I don't remember asking if anyone else was ok. When I watched Biggy I thought she was enjoying fussing around folk. She prayed for my dad, she helped my mum arrange the funeral. She opened her door to everyone. I didn't see her warm heart. I saw her stupidity. I didn't need her old-fashioned ideas or her fucking food. Or her constant redirection back to God. I needed my space.

This was my first rejection of Biggy. I had no problem crying but she was trying to force feed me this fucking soup and I was having none of it. Soup was her way of giving love. It was her I didn't want, her and all her sensible pre-programmed, society-friendly, Indian ideas.

There were those standard phrases:

'Be a good girl.'

'Look after your mum.'

'Pray to God.'

'Be educated.'

'Your mum sacrificed so much.'

This stuff is fine when you're a small girl, but it really used to piss me off.

My sister didn't cry, wouldn't cry, as you're supposed to, so they bullied her until she did. Their stock phrase is now banned now from our house: 'You've just become westernised!'

My dad died on the Sunday. I was back to school on Tuesday and told people I had a cold, until one of Biggy's stupid friends told her daughter my dad had died. Then the whole school knew. I was furious. Our relationship was already starting to fragment.

His dying made a huge change for everyone. The truth is we were relieved. Our relationship with Biggy and Granddad no longer had to be hidden. We could have Saturday nights there whenever we wanted.

But, ironically, they didn't happen anymore. I was out getting drunk. We had moved back to the family home and we had a telephone at last, but anytime Biggy called I was sullen. She didn't excite me anymore. She was just this stupid old woman who wanted to check up on me. But she wasn't really. She didn't impose and she didn't intrude. Seeing her and Papa Ji was a constant reminder of the roots I wished I had never had.

With further irony, by losing the man who should have protected me, I also lost my actual protector: Biggy. I lost my need for her and my respect. I now had other plans for Saturday nights.

There were other losses too. Three hours after my dad died, my Sikh boyfriend came round and dumped me. His parents had arranged for him to marry someone else. Biggy thought my dad had somehow magicked him away with him because he wouldn't have approved anyway. I began to go through boyfriends like they were going out of fashion. In Biggy's eyes I should be marrying an Asian boy, and not until I'd finished my education. Instead I went out with all sorts: long hair, skinheads, old men, smelly men, buskers, guys with cars, guys with no cars, guys with jobs and no jobs – all cultures and all colours.

All this kicked off just ten days before my Highers. I was always a diligent student – ten hours plus of studying at the weekend, every weekend. On Saturday I would get up early, study and then hit the pub at five. I'd start with a beer, then an alco-pop, then some shots. Afterwards possibly some chips and a vomit. My mum would pick me up from the pub at ten o'clock and take me home. She was disgusted by me, but still there and never saying a word. What could she have done? I would have gone anyway.

Around that time we had a discussion we both remember like it was yesterday. We were both, understandably, thinking about death a lot. I was obsessing about dead bodies, forensic pathology, serial killers and the like. I wasn't interested in the afterlife or God or anything like that, only the earthly side of things. Mum handled it quite well and was pragmatic enough to indulge my curiosity. Then one day she asked me a strange question.

'Who do you think will die first, Big Mama or Papa Ji?'

Can you imagine asking a child that?

The next question was:

'Which of the two of them would cope best with being left behind?'

This was a serious question so we both gave it serious consideration. We decided in the end that if Papa Ji died then Biggy would cope, because that's what Biggy did, she coped. But my Granddad, being a man, wouldn't manage at all with just daughters and nobody to take care of him.

'Big mama will always have us, you see,' said my mum. 'She'd manage.'

So, Biggy was the coper.

How wrong we were.

Dying is the only certainty in life. But as you grow up the idea of it becomes pretty scary. You try to catch the grains of time in your inconsequential day and struggle to pick up a few free moments and live. What must it be like to nurse your own decaying mind when it is inside a perfectly able body? To know you are slipping away but not losing consciousness? To have others around you look at you with their hopeless eyes exuding a mixture of pity and fear, to regress into stupidity, to have nobody listen to you because it doesn't make sense, even inside your own head, to have lived so much but to fail to appreciate how to wipe your own backside and to be dependent on the society you helped to create? Is psychic pain worth worrying about if you are going to forget you had it moments later? Is there any pain? Is there anything at all?

Chapter 6

We were free at last. It must have been a great joy to Big Mama and Papa Ji to see their daughter finally settled, back in her own home and living peacefully with her children.

They were getting older and had settled into a very comfortable routine. They'd get up early, get themselves dressed and then eat breakfast. They'd go to the day centre together, stay for lunch and come back in the afternoon. Then Papa Ji would have a nap while Biggy cleaned the house or sat on the floor of the living room, knitting, sometimes watching Eastenders. She was a big fan by then. At seven in the evening they would have something to eat and afterwards they would watch the nine o'clock news together. And that would be it. They'd go to bed shortly after. They managed very well.

But I didn't need her anymore and I had no time for her traditional ways, no interest.

A year passed peacefully in this way, with everyone just getting on with life, getting settled after all the turmoil of all the previous years.

And then it was the end of April with Papa Ji's birthday coming up. The family organised a mini party in their house as usual. We did this every year and every year he told us not to do it so we did it anyway! Unfortunately, my mum had just started a new job in a care home and couldn't ask for the night off, so none of our lot went. But Papa Ji always phoned everyone who couldn't be there, so he phoned her first before she went in to work. I was there with her and I didn't want to speak to him but she said 'Get on the phone!' so there was no choice. I'm glad now. My mum told Papa Ji she was off from work a couple of days later and we'd go over and have another celebration then. Celebrations are quite popular in my family. He also phoned my mum's sister in Canada and spoke to her family.

The following morning I was up on the exercise bike. I was waiting for my mum to come back from her night-shift and drive me to my job in another nursing home. It was 7am and as I frantically pedalled away, I looked up my horoscope. 'Do not be overwhelmed by a difficult situation which may take you by surprise,' it said. Not a good start to my day as a carer in a home.

The phone rang. We were used to Biggy calling every night, even quite late, but no way did anyone ever call at that time. Not ever. I knew there was trouble.

I went to pick it up.

'Hello?' I said.

But all I could hear was heavy breathing at the end of the phone. It was like someone was screaming but without any noise coming out, a horrible choking sound as if someone was being strangled.

'Hello? Who is this?' Prickles shot up the back of my neck.

Then the phone went dead.

'Oh my God, what the fuck is going on?' I said to the silence. 'I don't understand.'

I did 1471 and to my horror got Biggy's number. As I stood there with the phone in my hand, I felt a sort of hollowness in my legs, as if I had cycled too far and couldn't go on, but I knew that wasn't it. I could hardly dial for the trembling in my hand.

'Hello? Biggy? What's happening?'

'He's gone!' she said. 'He's gone!'

There was a pause while I wondered what she meant, though really I knew. Taking control of emergency situations is something I do every day now. Today I could do it standing on my head. Maybe this is where I learnt it.

'Where's Papa Ji?' I said.

'He's gone,' she said, between breaths, her voice hardly a whisper. 'He's gone!'

'Where?' I said.

'Gone,' she whispered.

'Is he lying down?' I said.

'Is he lying down?' she echoed.

'Biggy,' I said, as firmly as my voice would allow. 'Tell me where Papa Ji is.'

'On the bed,' she said.

'Is he breathing?'

She began to wail at this.

'Is he ok? Did he fall?'

The wailing continued, then, 'Yes, no, he's in bed. He went to the toilet …'

Then that choking sound.

'Ok. I'm going to call an ambulance. You go into the kitchen and boil up some tea and Mum and I'll be over straight away. Don't do anything else. Just sit tight.' I didn't know what else to say.

There was no answer then the phone went dead again.

I dialled 999 and told them what had happened then called my mum in the care home where she was doing a night-shift. Then I phoned a taxi and went straight there. But the ambulance, bless them, got there first by a whole ten minutes so poor little Big Mama had to deal with them all by herself. I was ten minutes late, as usual. Dammit. Mum was right behind me. But Papa Ji had died a long time before any of us got there.

Once there, I didn't know what to do and stumbled about the place like a fart in a trance. I don't remember comforting Biggy or what my mum did or what the ambulance people did. But I do remember standing in Big Mama's kitchen asking the medics whether there would be an autopsy or a murder enquiry. And once things had settled down we managed to get out of her what had happened.

She said they went to bed as usual after everyone went home and that at 4am he got up to go to the bathroom, like he always did. Then he came back into bed beside her as if nothing was wrong and went off to sleep. Papa Ji was like clockwork. Then he would always wake at seven. That was his time for waking up. But that morning, for the first time, he didn't. She tried to wake him.

'Why aren't you getting up?' she said to him, not understanding.

But no matter how hard she tried, he wouldn't waken and that's when she realised what had happened and lost the plot. That's when she phoned me.

Papa Ji died lying next to Big Mama, his great love, his

partner and companion for 53 years. She said that after he came back from the bathroom he never moved, never held out his hand to her to say 'Help me.' He didn't ask for anything, just went quietly, peacefully in his sleep.

'How come I didn't know?' she said. 'Why didn't I get up and help him? Why didn't he ask me to help? I would have helped him. Whatever he needed …'

She went to the pigeons on the ledge at the little back window in her house and spoke to them. Papa Ji used to feed them every day.

'No-one will feed you now,' she said sadly. 'The person who feeds you is gone.'

Much later on she was able to tell us more.

'It just proves what a good man he was and that he did something good in another life,' she said.

Hindus believe dying in your sleep means just that, that it was a reward for a previously worthy existence. She always held this was true of her son's little dog too, who also died in his sleep.

'And it shows he never suffered,' she said. 'Do you know, one of his last words will have been 'Om'. Do you know what that means?'

'Sort of,' I answered vaguely.

'It's the supreme name of God.'

'Yeah,' I said.

'It's how we know that God is the creator, preserver and destroyer of this universe.'

'Really?' I said. 'And why would Papa Ji say that then?'

'Because it's the soul leaving the body, of course. It was Papa

81

Ji's soul leaving his body.' She looked at the ground for second, lost in thought, then her brow crinkled and she gazed at me in bewilderment. 'But I didn't hear it? How come I never heard it?'

'Dunno, Biggy. Maybe he never said it.'

'Well of course he said it. Of course he did. I just don't understand why I didn't hear him.'

She shook her head again, completely baffled. I waited for her to go on but she didn't.

'You always said it was the best way to go,' I said. 'You know, in your sleep.'

'Oh, definitely. It is the best way. You don't cause anybody any suffering. You didn't ask for any help. You didn't suffer yourself.' Then she paused for a moment to think. 'But how come I didn't know?'

She still says this. She still doesn't understand. It still hurts.

Papa Ji was, of course, laid out in Big Mama's house and again people flooded in for the absose. This one wasn't as bad. I didn't feel as angry as I had at my dad's one. There may have been an obvious reason for this. I went with my mum to the airport to pick up her older sister from Canada and while I was there I bought half a bottle of gin and a half bottle of vodka. When we got back to Biggy's I stashed them in Big Mama's cupboard under her saris and proceeded to numb the pain, knocking them back when I thought no-one was looking and thinking how clever I was and why didn't they all just do the same? I mean that's what happens at Scottish funerals, so why not us? I honestly thought no-one would ever realise what I was up to.

It was Biggy herself who did. Why she was digging about

amongst her saris I don't know, but she found the bottles and brought them out.

'What is this?' she said, not understanding at first, a bottle in each hand. They just looked all wrong on her.

So, Big Mouth, yours truly had to defend herself, had to explain the logic of getting pissed as a way of coping, no, as a way of celebrating Papa Ji's life. Of course, this was Big Mama who'd never touched a drop in her life so she wasn't about to agree never mind join me in a wee 'swally' as it's known in these parts. Instead she just took me in her arms and hugged me. My mum on the other hand went ballistic and, I have to admit, if I'd been in her position I would have done the same.

The other thing I remember about that day, strangely, was Papa Ji's head. He was bald but he had a bit of hair on top that was sticking straight up at right angles. I kept trying to smooth it down but the hair wasn't having it. It just kept bouncing back up.

Biggy went grey that day. And at the funeral she just looked very old. It was like she changed colour completely. And she was cold and wet too, as if she was drowning in grief. She lost everything when she lost Papa Ji – her protector, her master, (though I know that sounds awful) her confidant and her home.

They asked me to make a speech in Punjabi on behalf of the five Grand-children, which I did. That was a hard thing to do, and no vodka this time. But the other four were lined up behind me like a solid wall of strength, so I got through it. Losing Papa Ji was easier than losing my dad because I had no conflict with him. He had lived a long and mostly happy life and we had always been close and fond of each other. But of course it wasn't like that for Biggy.

When I think back, now that I'm older and a psychiatrist, I think Biggy was in shock, and I think something left her when Papa Ji died and what can only be described as a vacancy took its place. That's the first time that I can pinpoint the same vacancy I see in her now. It was then that the terrible slide began. That's when she became vulnerable. She still says this all the time:

'The people that were supposed to be here have gone. My reason for living is dead. You don't need me any more so it's my time to go.' She said that back then and she still says it now.

In a funny way, her career, if you could call it her career, was the cooking, the house, being the homemaker, looking out for everyone else. But at that point, not only did she not pick it back up when her beloved Papa Ji died, she actively threw it away. When he went, all that homemaker stuff just stopped. I can understand that living on your own you don't necessarily want to cook for yourself, but she just gave up. I suppose she withdrew, even though she'd managed things like going to the post office, going to the bank, buying stuff, managing the finances things like that, for years. She'd always done all that very well. But with Papa Ji gone she fell to bits completely.

Now, of course, she's forgotten when Papa Ji died and we don't really remind her about it. There's no point. In the past we used to all go up on the day and sit together. We never mentioned it. We used to always do that on the day her son, my uncle, died. We simply made a point of being there. Although she's forgotten all that, we still made a point of being there in case she did remember. One time she did know the day because I remember her crying with me. She gave me a photo of him to keep, now framed and in my house. But she doesn't remember either of the anniversaries any more. It's not that she would want to forget. It's just that she isn't remembering things. That's the dementia.

She was never the same.

A person can lose everything in a turn of the wheel: lights go out, a new day starts, the calendar changes and the clocks tick. One day turns into the next and the years fly by. Finding yourself alone after walking hand in hand with someone your whole life must be incredibly exposing. What would there be to live for? It is easy for others to say 'just get on with it'. Maybe forgetting is a blessing; maybe it's best to sink. But it's hard to watch and painful to think about. We know nothing in life is free and that all good things, including lives, come to an end. Why then are we so shattered when we face the inevitable?

Papa Ji

Chapter 7

Did the slide into dementia start then, or was it just ordinary grief after losing Papa Ji? The distinction became blurred for me, partly because I was too busy living my own teenage life and getting myself as far away from Big Mama and all her advice as I possibly could. I thought that she fell to bits when he went and that she never recovered. I thought that, what with her being so traditional, when she lost her best friend, her protector, her companion and yes, I hate to say it, but her master, that her whole reason for being had dissolved. Or at least that was how I thought she may have seen it. But the truth is I wasn't really there to pass comment. How would I have known when boyfriends or hangovers were the most important thing in the world to me? I'm looking at everything in retrospect with the knowledge of a doctor – and an adult.

As soon as Papa Ji died our Saturday night routine vanished and nothing really took its place. I had better things to do. Watching TV while she knitted wasn't one of them. We'd had a routine until my Granddad died, but then suddenly there was no routine and none of us wanted to go any more. Mum and Anju Masi couldn't accept it:

'You need to start doing something for your Gran.'

'Isn't it time you went to see Biggy?'

I passed my driving test in 2001 so then it was 'Why don't' you go and pick Big mama up from the shops/bank/temple?' So sometimes I used to take her places or pick her up in the car and take her to the temple. Sometimes I'd even go in myself.

With Papa Ji's passing and his funeral came relatives and one of those was Bala, my mum's big sister, Biggy's eldest daughter, all the way from Canada. She comes regularly now, at least once or twice a year. As the eldest of the next generation she had to be listened to, so after the funeral she stayed a few weeks and took on the sorting of all Biggy's affairs. Decisions could not be made without her and one of those decisions included where Biggy was going to live.

When Biggy and Papa Ji moved to Scotland from Kenya all those years before, they bought a flat at 1159, Argyle Street in Glasgow's West End. It was a third floor flat on two levels with five bedrooms and panoramic views across the city. It was in a tenement building with other flats and a shared stairwell. Upstairs in the flat there were three bedrooms for their three daughters. The rest of the flat was downstairs including their bedroom, the spare bedroom, living room etc. I only ever saw this house once because they'd downsized to the two-bedroomed flat, all on one level, below it on the first floor by the time I came along. The only time I saw the upstairs was that time my dad said he thought he might buy it and took me to the viewing.

Big Mama's building had been emptying fast over the last couple of year because there was talk of renovations. Big Mama and Papa Ji had also been looking for somewhere else for a while but hadn't found anything suitable. On the ground floor were empty shops and above her the abandoned flat had filled up with 'junkies', so all sorts of people were coming and going.

In medical speak, we don't say 'junkies'. We commonly have terms like 'Intravenous Drug Misusers' or 'those with substance dependency'. It was Biggy who used the word 'junkie'. I am baffled as to where she might have picked it up, but it was Glasgow after all. 'Junkie' is also a funny word in a Punjabi accent. Of all the words she could have picked up! Maybe it was Billy Connolly? He's often blamed for Biggy's foul mouth.

The fact remained – she was a woman living alone without even neighbours to protect her. The family deemed it not safe for her to live there on her own any more. She would need to move.

She used to go out to these 'junkies' from upstairs and speak to them in her broken English:

'Don't do this. Just get out. You're not allowed to do this. This is a nice block of flats.'

She talked to them like she was the 'elder' and had the right to tell them what to do and as if they would listen and just do it. They ignored her, not saying or doing anything to her. One day she did actually chase one of them out of the close so, after that we thought it best to get her away from there as soon as possible.

My mum pulled out all the stops until a sheltered flat was found for her in a complex not far from where she'd lived for thirty-five years. It was handy for the shops, the buses and underground, the town centre and of course the temple. It had emergency cords which she could pull if she fell and which she coiled up and hung out of the way for the sake of tidiness. It had full central heating and a warden during office hours. There thirty-nine occupants in the same building, some of whom became friends, others not. She moved in less than a year after

Papa Ji died, taking the blue leather sofa and all her photographs with her.

'Papa Ji would have loved this place,' she said when she was all moved in.

She bought new carpets and other bits and bobs, and we decorated it. She, Anju Masi and my mum all thought it was brilliant because you could go around in your cardigan all day, it was so warm. It was easy to look after too and they didn't need to worry because of the warden. Plus my mum worked in the next street so she could be there at least twice a day.

But I always hated it. It was claustrophobically small and depressing. After Argyle Street it was like a prison. It smelled of urine, like an old folk's home. The washing machine was in the basement instead of in her own kitchen and it had a bloody stupid lift that took forever. You'd be pacing up and down waiting for it, trying to stay calm. It just wasn't Argyle Street.

We had Sky TV installed, after much wrangling with the warden and the local council. She liked her Zee TV, an Asian channel. Until she had Sky my mum used to record all her Asian programmes for her each evening and take them to her in the morning so she could watch them all on video. The workmen installed her Sky dish, my mum handed over £350 for the work, said thank you and waved goodbye. Biggy couldn't remember anybody being in her house. She kept asking my mum to take the extra channels away because she hadn't paid for them and that they belonged to someone else. No amount of reassurance calmed her down.

For the first three years after Papa Ji died she seemed to cope reasonably well. She did all the stuff he would have done, going to the bank and the post office, organising everything. I don't remember seeing her cry, though my mum did. It must have been a devastating loss after fifty three years of marriage. She was bewildered and still to this day can't understand what happened the awful night he died.

'Why didn't he call for me to help him? How could I lie next to him and not know?'

And then there were those times when she'd say 'I don't understand. All the people I am here to look after are gone. There's no reason for me to be here anymore. It's time for me to die.' This really upset me, when she talked like this. It upset us all.

In many ways this was normal, uncomplicated grief and Biggy got on with life because there was no other choice. She moved house, went to the temple and she even went to India by herself a couple of years later and took all Papa Ji's belongings to give to charity. We went to Canada at the same time to visit Bala and talked on the phone. I remember our conversation. Everything seemed to be more or less fine. She was just a little sad sometimes, nostalgic maybe.

'What happened to that lovely bride and groom ornament we had in Argyle Street?' she'd sometimes ask in a wistful way. 'I was keeping it for your wedding.'

I shuddered at the thought of a wedding let alone being made to display these two creepy looking mannequins in glass bell jars, trapped forever in their Asian attire.

So we'd tell her it went to charity, or was sold. I think my mum may have secretly binned it. That's what happens when you make decisions about other people's prized possessions, isn't it? One man's treasure: another man's junk.

'There's no room for it here anyway,' we'd tell her. 'And you don't need it now you're here.' 'Not now there's only you and not you and Papa Ji,' is what we meant. She'd be sad for a bit which was only to be expected.

Personally I found her massively annoying and embarrassing. I'm disgusted now when I think about this. For instance, my mum and I decided to go for lunch one day and nothing would stop us but it had to be Pizza Hut.

'But not the Drumchapel one, though,' I said. 'It'll be full of Asian's.' The temple day centre that Biggy went to sometimes took everyone there. It was their big treat. When they got there they all wanted extra chilli on their pizzas like a strange enactment of a cliché.

'No,' she said with great confidence. 'This is the wrong day for that.'

So guess who was in Drumchapel Pizza Hut? I had to do the rounds of all the 'aunties'. Everyone who is female and older and remotely connected to you, whether by blood or not is considered your auntie and worthy of respect, allowed to probe you for information 'So, you're the doctor. Good girl!' They have rights to kissing and pinching of cheeks too and to give advice to take better care of your mother/aunt/Gran. And there is no escape. This is roughly what Big Mama was trying to pull on the junkies in the close.

Younger me was mortified, furious at the public indignity I thought I was being subjected to. Older me is still mortified at

92

being so mortified and furious.

There was another incident around that time, this one in the temple. I'd just bought a little two-seater sports car and picked Biggy up at home to take her there.

'What did you pay for that thing?' she said, straight-faced.

So I told her how much, thinking I'd done quite well.

'You've been fleeced,' she said, but the twinkle in her eye gave her away. 'They've only given you two seats and it doesn't even have a roof. What use is that in Scotland? They saw you coming for sure.' She still had her sense of humour. That was a good thing.

I took her to the temple and ushered her in before me in style. We settled down with the others. I had gone to see if I could get whatever it was Biggy got from all this religion. I found something else instead.

A white student who was there for the day walked up to the deities at the front and made the sign of the cross, and then she backed away. She obviously didn't know what else to do. How could she? She did what was respectful in her culture and came away without turning her back to the altar. I thought that was very respectful and multi-cultural. But all the aunties round about us started saying 'Who does she think she is?' and 'How dare she?' and complaining about how disrespectful she had been to them.

Big Mama never said a word. She never had a bad word about anyone.

In my mind this little scenario set Biggy apart from the rest of them, far apart. I saw how accepting she was, how calm and loving towards everyone who came in her path. She just accepted them as they were and didn't pass judgement, sat there as cool and calm as you like with her heart still pumping out love and acceptance for all.

'We don't know what kind of pain or suffering these people have inside themselves,' she said. 'They're no doubt doing their best.'

In my great fiery wisdom, I missed, temporarily, her great watery wisdom. I thought she was being wise but foolish, that's how clever I was! But I never went back, not once. I absolutely refused to. I still won't. 'I can find God in the toilet, Biggy. Apparently he's everywhere,' I'd proclaim in my fluent Punjabi. Biggy would roll her eyes. She never forced anything on anyone, even though it felt like you were getting a constant lecture. At least she had the faculties to lecture me then.

One day a small disaster struck that seemed to signal something worse and Biggy began to unravel, very slowly, like one of her carefully knitted jumpers. It took a while for us to realise. Perhaps she had been unravelling since Papa Ji died.

She liked to go to a cheap department store in town and buy daft things for us, like costume jewellery, old-lady clothes or cleaning mitts for the car! Why would anyone want to buy a thing like that? But this day she had been crossing the road and didn't see that the lights had changed. A car had come round the corner and clipped her and she had fallen over. I got a phone call from the Royal Infirmary, near where I was working. I bolted up there and saw her. She was in A & E and suffering terrible pain. This was the first time I had ever heard her complain about pain.

She'd never had a physical ailment or health problem in her life. It heralded a period where she became increasingly worried with her physical wellbeing, compulsively talking about every ache and pain, her medication and then starting to have panic attacks.

Immediately after the accident she went to stay with my mum and got thoroughly looked after until she was well enough to go back to her sheltered housing. We kept a much closer watch on her. As she began to obsess about her health, so did we, especially my mum who was on the front line. I guess my mum felt the loss of Papa Ji more keenly than the next generation and was in no hurry to lose Big Mama too.

The first thing my mum worried about was depression. She felt Biggy maybe got stuck sometimes being sad or anxious and that it wasn't just bereavement. This was discussed with all the family, as usual. No-one agreed. But my mum felt strongly about it and took her to the GP who prescribed anti-depressants. Again the family met round the table. Bala Masi was over from Canada and everyone argued like crazy.

'She's going to be low after an accident. She'll be fine in a few weeks or months,' said Preity.

'No, this has gone on too long. She's not paying any attention to her Grand-children,' said my mum.

'That's because they're not paying any attention to her,' said Anju Masi.

'Yes, we are!'

'You know perfectly well you're not. You treat your patients better than you treat your own Grandmother!'

This is what we have all said to one another over the years.

'You're a doctor/nurse/pharmacist. You wouldn't treat your patient or customers like this. You're a disgrace for a daughter/Granddaughter etc!' Fill in the blanks as appropriate. It's what Big Mama has been known to say to us too. But the argument raged on.

'She's not ill. She's shaken.'

'Anti-depressants would help get her back to normal more quickly.'

'She's a strong capable woman. There's nothing wrong with her.'

'She's a strong capable woman who's depressed.'

'She's a strong capable woman who's grieving, who's lost her husband and her home and been hit by a car. She needs anti-depressants.'

'She's a strong capable woman who's grieving and got a fright but who's managing very well in the circumstances.'

'Maybe it's dementia,' I said. Actually I have no idea why I brought it up. I didn't know much about dementia except from textbooks and bits and pieces from anatomy lectures at the university. I had no real evidence for saying it.

'Don't be ridiculous,' they all said. 'Dementia? She's just a bit shaken.'

And so it went on. And so I agreed she was depressed, although I didn't really know much about that either, but I didn't think she should be on anti-depressants. Looking back, luckily, in my opinion, Biggy didn't take the anti-depressants because the family decreed it.

She carried on going to the day centre at the temple and doing her own shopping in KRK, the local Asian shop, and everything went on as normal, although we were all a little more edgy.

Some kind of anxiety had set in. Her leg hurt, her back hurt. She had a cold, perhaps it was pneumonia. What was this ache? That pain? Could it be … dare we mention it … cancer? And so began a round of physical health checks from every department in the NHS. Biggy was tested from top to bottom.

And of course the family arguments continued round the tables of our houses and favourite restaurants. The discussions were heated, explosive even. But that's the nature of a strong family bond. There's never anything final about these arguments. Not even the decisions that are made!

It's hard to estimate how much the human body can take. It's even harder to comprehend what a mind can bear. Life is full of expectations and it is easy to look back at the trajectory of an illness and think you have found the source. 'Grief-loss-death. That's it! That's the trigger. That's why she lost her mind.' The truth is that dementia is like any other illness. It is unlike every other illness too. We couldn't have predicted, saved or prevented it. It would have happened, regardless of the story, of the events up until now. Educated or not, religious or not, English speaking or not, it could happen to anyone. Still, it's human nature to ask, even though I don't know who I am asking: why her, why my Biggy?

Chapter 8

Biggy had some strong opinions on all this. She was most vocal on the 'You're a doctor/nurse/pharmacist. You wouldn't treat your patients or customers this way.' To begin with, this was mostly directed at my mum and Anju Masi because the rest of us were usually nowhere to be seen. But whenever we did appear, the accusations would fly, Big Mama, Anju Masi and Mum all having a go.

Some of this was the usual stuff of the 'respect your elders' or 'be a good girl' variety, which had me screaming. That's stuff's fine when you're five. It doesn't work so well once you're past twenty and doing a degree in medicine.

The main reason for all this aggro was that Big Mama was not herself. She had started behaving oddly but didn't seem to know she was doing anything out of the ordinary. To us it seemed deliberate to begin with, like she was just being difficult or, being kinder, asserting her right to do things her own way.

When she first moved to the new flat she fed the birds outside the front of the complex, taking bread to them and leaving it in a pile. This was another thing Papa Ji would have liked. But the warden and the local council didn't like it at all.

'It's a health hazard,' everyone said. 'You'll attract vermin.'

So she waited until he was gone then fed them round the back of the building. If I happened to be there, she'd beckon me round there as if she had some kind of contraband in her bag, throw bread at me and make me feed them too. It was a game she enjoyed massively. Until the Chinese man who lived next door realised what she was up to and a huge argument erupted. They never really made up.

She had another neighbour, a Muslim lady who had no visitors and watched jealously whenever we arrived. She would often mysteriously appear not long after us and try and join the gathering, but Big Mama was having none of it.

'Go away. They're my visitors, not yours,' she'd say and send the poor woman packing. This was sad, of course it was, but the woman was so persistent and Biggy so adamant that it was hard not to laugh. This was not the generous-hearted Big Mama we'd known all our lives. It was another early indicator that something wasn't right.

As Biggy's anxiety rose, so did her phone bill. She phoned us many times a day, often in a panic.

'My heart's jumping!' she'd tell my mum. 'It's beating too fast. My heart's beating. It's jumpy. You need to take me to hospital. You need to take me to the doctor. You're a terrible daughter. How could you let me get into this state?' She'd be wheezing between all the words. 'Help! I need a doctor!'

'Don't be silly. It's nothing of the sort,' my mum would say. 'Just calm down and stop shouting at me. I'll get the doctor. Have you eaten anything? What did you have to eat? I'll phone Pinky.'

'It's not my stomach, stupid. It's my heart! Why don't you listen to me? I bet you listen to your patients. You're terrible to your own mother.'

So my mum would phone me in a panic of her own.

'She's says her heart's jumping,' she'd say, all the time wheezing as she said it. 'She thinks she's having a heart attack. What do you think?'

'What's the matter with you?' I'd say. 'You sound terrible. Are you breathing all right?' I could hear the panic in her voice, hear her losing her breath. 'Slow down, Mum, I can't understand you. Where's Biggy? Is she with you? Mum! Mum?'

And then I'd start to panic too.

'What's the matter, Pinky?' she'd gasp. 'You sound breathless.'

By the time we'd finished with this, we were all three of us breathless and exhausted.

So we took her to the doctor and the doctor said her lungs were fine.

Our phone bills continued to reach ridiculous proportions.

Then one day when Anju Masi and I came to visit Big Mama, there was a Lidl shopping trolley in the middle of the living room floor.

'Biggy?' I said. 'Have you taken to stealing now?'

How we laughed.

Big Mama didn't see the joke at first. So there was a shopping trolley in her living room. What was the problem? In what way was that abnormal?

Once we'd calmed down and Anju Masi had taken a photo of me in the trolley, we managed to get some sort of story out of her. Basically she had filled her trolley with goods, paid at the check-out (that was a relief), and set off for home. Why did no-one stop her? The most amazing thing about it was the fact that there are two huge main roads to be crossed and several very high curbs to be negotiated between Lidl and her home. But luckily a 'little student' had seen her struggling and offered to help. She had helped her all the way home and into the very, very, very slow lift. She'd even helped her out of it again and into her flat. Biggy was quite triumphant.

But the second Lidl incident wasn't so funny.

This time Biggy had her bath, got dressed, put on her coat, lifted her bag and set off for her weekly shop. The time on her clock was ten o'clock. She cut across the two main roads and through the back streets, past several pubs which seemed unusually busy where lots of people were outside smoking. They seemed quite drunk, but this was nothing to concern her so on she went. She didn't notice that there wasn't much traffic or that it was dark and all the local shops were shut. As was Lidl.

She turned round and retraced her steps and, safely back home, phoned my mum.

'Lidl's is shut,' said Biggy, still surprised. 'Why would Lidl be shut?'

'It's midnight!' said my Mum.

Mum phoned me, laughing, to pass on the latest funny story. It wasn't funny.

'That's not funny, Mum,' I said. 'That's dangerous. Anything could have happened. She shouldn't be at home on her own.'

'Don't be silly,' she said. 'She was perfectly safe.'

'That's not the point. How did she manage to get her day and her night back to front? Why didn't she notice it was dark?'

'Right enough,' she said. 'Maybe there's something wrong with her eyes.'

'Her eyes?' I yelled. 'It's not her eyes. It's dementia!'

'No, it's not,' she said. Not laughing now. 'It's not dementia.'

'Yes, it is,' I said. 'I'm a doctor. It's dementia.'

'How would you know? You never go and see her.'

So we had her eyes tested and guess what? They were fine. Another family meeting was called. Everybody argued, nobody agreed, nothing was decided.

'She's not as sharp as she used to be. She's just old. This is normal.'

'She's not been well. Old people sometimes get confused when they get the flu or the cold.'

'Why are you so determined it's dementia? That's a terrible thing to suggest about your own Gran.'

'But there's medication for it now,' I said. 'It can slow down the process. We need to get it checked as soon as possible.'

'You medicalise everything.' This was my brother, Raj, a lawyer who normally stays out of it and is one of the few of us not in the medical world. 'She's just a bit dotty. Leave her alone.'

So everybody went home and nothing was done.

And then Deepa arrived, back from Manchester for a few days. It was much colder than she'd expected so she put on one of Biggy's 'fancy' cardigans, an ugly thing with embroidery and sequins all over the place which my mum had taken home to hand wash. She and I started impersonating Biggy.

'Honour your parents,' we said in Biggy's Punjabi accent. 'Wear their clothes.'

'Stop that, you two,' chided my mum, but she was laughing too. Then she went to pick up Biggy.

'Oh, you look lovely!' said Biggy when she arrived.

'Thank you,' said Deepa. 'It's a lovely cardigan.'

'Yeah, the purple matches the shadows under your eyes,' I said.

'What was that?' said Big Mama.

'Oh no, her hearing's going now,' said my mum.

'It's a beautiful cardigan,' Deepa cut in. 'That's what Pinky said.'

'No I didn't. It's pot ugly.'

Most people would agree that Deepa is Big Mama's favourite. But then Big Mama gets more kisses and cuddles from Deepa than anyone else. She loves the rest of us too but Deepa arrives, fusses over her in every way, and then disappears back to Manchester, a vision of saintliness.

'Keep the cardigan. It suits you so well,' said Big Mama.

'No, no,' says Deepa. 'I'm just getting warm. I'll give it back to you when I leave.'

'No, no,' says Biggy. 'It's yours. You have it. It's so lovely on you.'

So Deepa is the proud new owner of a purple embroidered sequined cardigan from last year's fashion parade.

None of this would have mattered except that Biggy forgot the whole incident and the next day demanded her cardigan back.

'You gave it to me,' said Deepa, not a little peeved.

But Biggy was adamant. 'Trying to steal off your old Gran!'

Mum demanded she return it too. 'Come on Deepa, for the sake of peace, just give it back. She didn't mean to give it to you.'

But Deepa was adamant too. Biggy got furious. I tried to

intervene.

'What do you want that ugly old thing for anyway?' I said.

Upon which all three turned on me.

'Pinky! Don't be so rude. It's a beautiful cardigan.'

Upon which I shrugged and went to make myself a coffee, but I could hear the argument raging, doors being slammed. Then, at dinner time, the gloves were off and the cardigan was on.

'You should make her give me it back to me!' said Big Mama whose behaviour was more appropriate to her height than her years. She repeated this several times through the starter, about twice for each pakora. Deepa wrapped the cardigan across her chest and kept eating. Half way through the main course the food had heated Deepa from the inside and the cardigan was off. Biggy eyed it across the table where it hung over the back of Deepa's chair. So did my mum. I considered grabbing it first and stashing it somewhere, like you would with badly-behaved children. While we were clearing the table and washing up, my mum did just that.

There was a row, with Deepa and Big Mama demanding the cardigan be given back immediately.

'She gave it to me!' said Deepa.

'I did nothing of the kind,' retorted Biggy. 'Thieving in your own home, from your own family. What have we come to?' She wailed and cried. Finally everyone was too exhausted to continue and went to bed. Biggy had never shouted in all her life. What on earth was going on?

The following day we left Biggy in the house while we went shopping and when we came back the whole place had been turned upside down. Biggy had searched everywhere and was sitting straight-backed like the queen, wearing the purple, embroidered, sequined cardigan with a defiant smile on her face. Everyone began shouting, myself included.

But visits to or from Biggy were not always that eventful. Usually they were excruciatingly empty. Five minutes in I'd be wishing I was somewhere else, willing the clock to go faster or wanting a big hole to open up and swallow me. I didn't want to be there. I hated her for being who she was. I hated her for not taking better care of her mind. I hated her for being so useless and yet still alive. It hurt me when she wished herself dead and yet I still wished she was gone. This whole period was massively painful for me because I didn't know what to think or feel. All I knew was that I didn't want to be anywhere near her, as if her uselessness was contagious. I dreaded every visit but was wracked with guilt when I didn't go.

I hated her but I loved her. I was a doctor so I should have been able to be more caring, but I couldn't. It felt false and I didn't want to be false. She was my Gran, but actually no, she wasn't. She was a shell, an empty vessel and she, herself, was gone. It was like she was already dead, but she wasn't.

When I visited, the conversation was always the same.

'How are you?' she'd say.

'Fine,' I'd answer.

'Are you ok?' she'd ask.

'Yes, fine.'

'Have you eaten?'

'Yes.'

105

'Oh,' she'd say. 'Do you want to eat something?'

'No thanks.'

'I got some mango for you. I cut it up just how you like it.'

'No thanks.' I never pointed out to her it was my mum or Anju who brought the mango and cut it up for her. She thought she'd done it herself for me.

'Or some pakora? I made some pakora specially for you.' Again, it was my mum's.

'Well, ok then.' I'd say this to give her something to do, something to break the awkwardness, having no idea what to say or do. I couldn't bear it.

It was slightly easier when she visited me because of the cats. She loves cats. It's an Asian thing, the belief that the cat chooses the owner and not the other way round. When I first got my two, Schnookums and Clive, she took one look at Schnooky and smiled her big beautiful smile.

'You've done something for her in a past life,' she said. 'Or you owe her in some way. She's back here for you to take care of her. You must take very good care of her always.'

This is something I'm very happy to do.

Schnooky was all over her as well.

Big Mama smiled all over her face. She was so happy and, actually, so lucid that day. She bonded so thoroughly with my beautiful Schnookums that I got in touch with the Cats Protection to see if Schnookums could become a cat therapist with dementia sufferers.

Result? Well, no, actually, because meanwhile the battle in my head raged on. I could do it for complete strangers but still dreaded seeing my own Gran who had protected me and nurtured me and made me what I am, a highly successful, professional woman in a job which is challenging and which I love, using my brain even though she never seemed to have used hers. It's shameful how I neglected her during this period and how I left it all to my mum and Anju. We all did.

'Why are you not going?' they reproached us.

'I'm too busy with work just now,' I'd say every time. 'I'm exhausted and every minute there's a crisis with one of my patients. I'm on call.'

But I wasn't too busy. I was being driven only by fear. Somebody warned me at the time, 'You don't want to end up feeling guilty when she's gone. You'll regret not going.'

I had no idea if this was true or not, whether I would or wouldn't regret it or whether not going made me a callous person with no heart or not.

The crazy episodes continued, like the laundry caper, for instance. Biggy has always done her washing on a Friday. According to Big Mama, pants have to be washed in the bath, so her pants continued to be washed in the bath. But Biggy had no idea what day it was so, instead of never doing it, every day was a laundry day and Biggy's smalls got washed every single day. And because it's her short-term memory that is affected, she'd start the bath running and forget about it. We lost count of the number of times she flooded the downstairs neighbour.

She had also always washed her curtains once a week and this involved climbing up on the furniture and taking them down herself. This was done several times a week as well and naturally, this caused some alarm, Big Mama being 83 at the time. She bought Biggy some blinds and while she was at the day centre, climbed up there herself, took the curtains down and installed these lovely easy-to-use blinds. Biggy went ape-shit.

'Where are my curtains?' she wailed. 'Why would someone steal my curtains? What are these stupid things?'

'Blinds, Mum, they're blinds. It'll be easier to use. You won't have to climb on the furniture anymore.'

'Give me back my curtains!' she shrieked.

'This is much safer,' pleaded my mum.

'How could you take my curtains?' said Biggy.

So the curtains were reinstalled and Biggy continued to climb. We got her a little step-ladder to make it slightly less dangerous.

Biggy needed her curtains for a reason. My mum had phoned me one Sunday to tell me Big Mama had been very agitated of late, asking for 'the children'. She didn't mean my generation, she meant her own children, but my mum thought sending in the Grandchildren might pacify her. Or at least help her get some kind of time perspective. So I said I'd go in every Monday and give her lunch. This was another of our plans that quickly went astray.

'Ok, but you need to watch her,' Mum said. 'She's running about the house doing this naked thing. She's been doing it for ages.'

So the next day, there she is answering the front door to me completely stark staring naked, as the day she was born.

'Biggy!' I said, hurrying in so I could shut the door. 'You can't do that! Why are you standing there with no clothes on?' I didn't know where to look.

'I was just going to get dressed,' she said. I could see this wasn't true by the glint in her eye.

I followed her into the living room where the curtains were wide open giving a full view of Big Mama in all her glorious wrinkles to the neighbours across the street. She was on the first floor, right opposite lots of other flats. I rushed to close the curtains and protect her modesty.

'What are you doing this for?' I said, horrified.

'Why are you closing the curtains in the middle of the day?' she said. 'It's broad daylight.'

'Everyone can see you!'

'So what?' she said. 'I've got an old, withering body. Who's going to want to look at me?'

'It's kind of hard not to look,' I said, screwing up my eyes.

'I was only going from the bathroom to the living room to get my clothes,' she said.

'No, you weren't.'

'And then I'll go into the bedroom and get dressed.'

It was hilarious really, or maybe I was hysterical, because five minutes later, when I was still trying to persuade her to stop arguing and get dressed, the doorbell went again. If I hadn't arrived before him, the electrician who was coming to check the faulty fans would have found her naked on the door step. In fact, when he got there she went straight into the bedroom and put her clothes on. The thing is that if she hadn't answered the door, the warden would have come in to check she was ok and found her starkers anyway.

109

'Nobody wants to look at an old prune like me anyway. What difference does it make? Lots of people like to be naked in their own home,' she said.

Once I'd calmed down and stopped laughing, I saw how scary this actually was, how vulnerable she really was, how out of touch with normality. I remembered what she always used to say to me when I was wee, about the official order to put your clothes on in the morning, how pants always had to go on first because nobody can see 'down there'. This new habit was just weird.

I found myself almost having a schizophreniform voice (or what people expect from Schizophrenia anyway). I'm in conflict with myself all the time, because even when I see her I think, 'Why don't I spend some more time with my Gran? She's so lovely!' And then when my mum says 'Go up and see her,' I don't want to. I hate her but I love her. I'm a doctor. I should be more caring, but I can't. Why should I be false? This is my Gran. No, it's not. She's dead. No she isn't. Come on get a grip. She wants to die – why isn't God taking her? Why aren't we letting her go? I would rather she died happy and dignified than naked and misunderstood. She says she's done her life's work. Part of me can't see that. What life's work? Then I look at my family and I see that she actually brought up intelligent, free-thinking, free-spirited human beings. She did that. Why can't I be grateful?

Chapter 9

Dementia isn't all doom and gloom. Not long after the naked incident we had Diwali, our Hindu festival of light. This is actually a very beautiful festival involving lots of candles, new clothes and sweets. There are also various family traditions and rituals including the singing of a prayer which has lots of verses and chapters and is a bit like the Lord's Prayer. Big Mama loves all this.

We were in her house with the candles lit for my namesake, Lakshmi, goddess of light, beauty, good fortune and wealth. I've hoped some of this has rubbed off on me! You are expected to clean the house until it sparkles, as a welcome, something no-one has to do when I'm visiting. Biggy's house was always spotless anyway.

There were little oil burners in clay pots with scented oil all around the house and plenty of flowers. We were all there, Deepa and Raj, and Preity and Dhruv my cousins, and my mum, Anju Masi and her husband Yogi Uncle, all of us together singing the prayer. Big Mama was beaming, brim full of happiness. Us kids, on the other hand, were bored senseless with the whole thing and just wanted to get on with the food, or back to the Playstation or the TV. We were only standing there for the sake of duty and so as not to upset anyone. The main prayer lasts for about ten minutes which is an eternity in the life of a young person.

'*Sukh sampati ghar ave; kashta mite tan ka,*' we chanted.

'Peace and prosperity come home; problems of the body disappear.'

As the head of the family, and the most enthusiastic, Biggy lead the singing and when she sang the same verse twice we three glanced at each other, sniggered and joined in.

'Peace and prosperity come home; problems of the body disappear.'

The third time round we laughed out loud and got a finger waggled at us by Anju Masi.

The fourth time we snorted, then got bored and started eyeing up my mum's fab pakoras, piled high on a plate. Deepa lost control completely and was laughing so hard she could hardly stand up.

By the fifth circuit we were all wetting ourselves and about the no matter what Anju Masi or Mum or Yogi Uncle did to stop us. Big Mama appeared to be oblivious. She paused politely, her eyes ran over us as we giggled like five year olds, then went on with the next verse.

I turned to look at Deepa. She had tears all down her face. Thinking she was crying with laughter, I laughed all the more. But then I saw her shoulders shake and her mouth go and I realised: she wasn't laughing any more, she was crying. It took me a while to stop crying myself after that. Raj, Dhruv and Preity had stopped laughing too but they didn't get it, how tragic it was. Deepa and I huddled together and we all went on singing the prayer until it was finished.

We haven't been together as the whole family since then and Big Mama had already mostly stopped going to the temple by this point. When she did go and repeated the verses there too, my mum used to help her through it saying 'You've done that bit already, Mum. Move on.'

Although she didn't go to the temple often, she'd still sit at home and read the scriptures. One time I went to see her she was sitting reading a prayer book. What she was actually doing was reading it and re-reading it thinking that people were coming to pay respects for my Granddad just having died. It was so sad. Luckily this phase passed quickly. She began to lecture us less about that time which was a very good thing.

Despite all this, my mum and Anju Masi were planning a trip to India for her.

'One last time,' they said.

'Are you crazy?' I said. 'She doesn't want that.' Every time the India trip was brought up, we'd have another bout of those breathless phone calls.

'Yes, she does,' they said.

'No. This is about you. You want to take her there. She doesn't want to go.'

'We'll ask Bala when she gets here from Canada then.'

'Good,' I said. 'We can talk about her dementia then as well and what's to be done.'

So Bala, the oldest of the three sisters, arrived a few weeks later to discuss Biggy. A family meeting was called. Mum and Anju Masi filled the table with food and everyone sat down. Big Mama, of course, was not part of this discussion.

'I'm not talking about Big Mama without her being here,' said Raj, always a stickler for the law of fairness. 'We can talk all we like but it's all worthless if she doesn't get to be part of the discussion and agree on the outcome.'

'Big Mama doesn't know her arse from her elbow some days,' I said. 'That's the whole point.'

'She'll want to stay where she is,' said my mum. 'I'm only working round the corner. I don't know what all the fuss is about.' She yawned big and wide.

'You're exhausted!' I said. 'You can't keep on doing this.'

'Nonsense,' she said. 'I'm just off night shift. Of course I'm tired.'

I caught eyes with Deepa across the table and we both frowned.

'If you kids would just do more it would be a lot easier for us to manage,' said Mum. And then Anju Masi and Bala joined in berating us. Yogi Uncle stared at the ceiling.

Deepa and I exchanged glances and we kids chewed our lips.

'I've got loads of on-calls coming up,' I said, 'and a huge child protection case.' I tried to keep the panic out of my voice. It wasn't about work. 'It's constant just now,' I assured them. My mind wandered to the forthcoming weekend away with Stephen, thinking it couldn't come quick enough. 'And anyway we can't be there all the time. It's the times we're not there that she goes off piste and …'

'We should have a rota, do it in shifts,' said Mum, always the nurse.

'I can't do day shift,' we all said in unison.

'I'd just always be letting everyone down at the last minute,' I said quickly. 'You know what on-calls are like.' Actually the on-

114

calls had been quiet of late but I knew that wouldn't last. I realised I'd rather go to an on-call with some disturbed and aggressive teenager than visit my own Gran. What a disgrace I was.

'Day-time isn't the time we need to worry about,' put in Bala, who hadn't got over the alarm of the midnight Lidl incident.

'It was daytime when she walked out in front of a car,' I said.

'Och, that was ages ago,' said Anju Masi.

'I don't think a rota's practical,' Deepa began, in her sensible voice. 'Three of us are already on shifts and I worked seventy hours last week. Plus I'm in Manchester.' Deepa had just finished her finals and had recently started as a junior doctor, the dogsbody of the medical world.

'We need her to be well enough by the summer for the trip to India,' said Mum.

'Well, that's never going to happen,' I said.

'Come on, Pinky, stop being so negative,' said cousin Dhruv. 'She just needs to get out more, get some exercise.' Well, he would say that, wouldn't he, being a fitness instructor. 'It'll probably be her last time.'

'Thanks for that,' Mum and I said together.

'If she just ate less,' said Deepa, munching on another pakora. 'It could be her weight affecting her heart.'

'Oh, yes,' said Mum. 'I'll phone the doctor in the morning and get her checked out. We don't want anything to happen on the flight.'

'She's not going,' I said. 'She isn't going to be well enough. She isn't going to get well. She won't know where she is. She … '

'Of course she'll know where she is,' said Anju Masi. 'She's been to India loads of times. She was born there, for heaven's sake. I don't know why you're making such a fuss.'

'She freaks out every time anyone mentions going to India,' I said. 'You guys just won't face the truth.'

'When did she last get her medication checked?' said Deepa, steering us away from the India trip.

So a long discussion ensued about the medication she was on, the side-effects, the other medication she could be on, the likely benefits, the possibility of all this just being a urinary infection, a heart/lung/blood/skin/dietary/gynaecological problem or a simple but persistent case of flu.

'What about her thyroid,' said Deepa. 'She's been a bit sluggish lately.'

'You'll be fucking sluggish when you're in your eighties,' I said, picking up a large slice of cake.

'Pinky, don't swear. You know I don't like it when you swear.'

'I fucking hate it too,' said Raj.

'Raj!' said mum, Anju, Bala and Yogi Uncle.

'It could just be dementia,' I ventured, very quietly, carefully, one last try once they'd all calmed down.

'There's no test for that,' said Anju Masi, as if that settled it as not being a possibility.

'There is medication,' said Yogi Uncle tentatively.

'She's not demented,' said Anju Masi.

'Yes, she is!' I said.

'So let's start from the beginning,' said Bala, ignoring me. 'Tell me everything you've done so far. Tell me everything that's happened.'

I went to make more coffee and to growl at my reflection in the window.

When I went back in they were laughing at the Diwali repetition, and citing their own forgetfulness as proof that Big Mama was just like them only more so.

'Nothing to worry about really,' said Mum.

'She needs residential care,' I said. Just to be clear. 'If she stays where she is she's going to have an accident of some kind. Or fall prey to some weirdo who'll take all her money off her or worse. Or she'll fall. She'll fall off the step-ladder when she's getting the curtains down every second day. I mean what's the statistical likelihood of an elderly lady falling off a ladder? My window cleaner fell off his last week, for fuck's sake, and he's been up ladders all his life. Something's going happen. She's demented. Why can't you fucking see that?'

'I can't believe you're saying this about your own Gran,' said Anju Masi. 'It's a shocking disrespect. And will you stop swearing? Look how you're upsetting your mum.' And everyone joined in giving me a hard time for swearing.

'There's nothing wrong with her physically,' I said, making no apology. I'd heard them all swear plenty of times. 'It's her mental function that's all over the place. Remember my engagement party? She danced all night!'

This is what actually happened. Stephen and I got engaged a while back and organised a big party to celebrate. Biggy had met Stephen and liked him, but she didn't want to go. Looking back I think the strain of pretending everything was alright was taking

117

its toll. Biggy knew something was wrong. She knew she couldn't remember things, and she was embarrassed. Plus it must have been exhausting playing all these silly games so we wouldn't notice. When Mum went to pick her up she wasn't even dressed (not naked this time, fortunately, just not ready) and refused to budge off the blue leather sofa. Eventually, through gentle persuasion and a few insults, she got off the sofa and put on her best sari and her best smile and arrived at the venue late but as if nothing had happened. The only evidence was my mum's face which was livid, drawn, exhausted and resigned all at the same time. Biggy proceeded to charm the pants off everyone, smiling like royalty and poking fun at us all. Our friends loved her. Her main form of charm attack was to take to the dance floor (after much persuasion) and dance for the rest of the night. She was mental, by which I mean daft and raring to go. She was up there dancing, proper dancing, all night long, proving she was physically extremely fit.

Then she refused to leave. And I mean 'refused to leave'. The DJ was booked until midnight but Biggy wasn't for stopping.

'It's bed-time,' said my mum. 'Come on. You're exhausted.'

'No, no,' she said. 'I'm very happy dancing. It's alright. I'm not tired at all.'

Now my friends all think she's the cutest thing in the world. You'd never have known her brain was rotting inside her head.

At our big family discussions on Biggy's future, I decided I had enough of denial and pretence.

'You're delusional, all of you,' I said. 'I don't know how you can't see it.' This was in fact a bit rich considering I didn't really

118

know that much about dementia myself. My work is with teenagers. The family weren't slow to point this out. At last someone saw sense.

'I think she's got a point, you know,' said Bala, bringing the room to quiet again. 'Not that you're delusional,' she added hastily, and all the angry faces relaxed. 'But Big Mama needs somewhere safe and comfortable with someone keeping an eye on her round the clock.'

There was a shocked silence.

'No …' said Anju Masi after probably a full minute. 'She's not that bad.'

'I don't see why,' said Mum.

'She needs twenty four hour attention, not just office hours,' said Bala. 'I don't know what's wrong with her because I'm not a doctor or a nurse, but I can see she's not safe on her own.'

'But …' said Anju Masi.

'Look at the lot of you,' said Preity, who was only sixteen. Everyone stared at her in surprise. What could she possibly have to add? 'You're all completely exhausted. This is not just for Biggy.'

This was true. Everyone works hard in my family and sometimes we don't know how to stop. I was certainly keeping busy so I didn't have to visit Big Mama. But Anju and Mum were run ragged going back and forwards, doing everything they could to keep her in her own home: leaving dinners carefully labelled with the day in her fridge, even though she always forgot what day it was, taking her to the temple, organising everything she needed or did, visiting all through the day, taking her out to places.

I went to the kitchen again and smiled at myself in the window, thankful for Preity and Bala, then brought fresh coffee for everyone. Nursing homes, residential homes, respite care, live-in care: all this was discussed. Living with us in rotation was also discussed briefly, but dropped, thank God. Mum and I have both worked in care homes and Anju Masi has been in loads because of working at Yogi Uncle's pharmacy, so, once care was decided upon, the men left us to decide what kind of care Big Mama needed.

Mum was sullen, resigned, wouldn't speak to me and barely spoke to Bala.

But that's what was decided: care. We'd decided together with Bala having the final throw.

Bala went back to Canada. Mum and Anju Masi went to see residential homes and I went too occasionally. None of the places was perfect, so we couldn't agree. But instead of making a decision, weighing up the pros and cons and choosing the best one, Mum and Anju Masi decided to get Bala back over and let her decide. Argh! I wanted to scream.

We took Big Mama out for dinner – to Chillies as usual, Biggy's favourite. Predictably Biggy wasn't ready when Mum went to get her. Mum persuaded and cajoled and finally ordered her to get dressed, then helped her to do it. As usual they were late, but this time Biggy didn't arrive smiling. Minus her central cheery disposition, we sat round the table bickering and arguing.

'What a terrible way to treat your own mother!' said Biggy. 'Terrible. You're a bad daughter. You have no respect. Everyone

120

thinks you're so kind, but it's not true. I know it's not true! You're bad. So bad!'

Mum sank down into her chair through all this with her head in her hands. There was a terrible pause. Biggy's words hung in the air. None of us could understand what was going on. This wasn't Biggy and her big heart, or Mum and her fiery defence of herself, or the rest of us her happy jokey family.

Suddenly my mum stood up.

'She's right,' she said. 'It's all my fault. Everything would be all right if it wasn't for me. You'd all be having a great old time if I wasn't here. So I'm going.'

And she left. And we all sat there watching her go with our mouths open. Gob-smacked. Which is not like us at all.

'Good riddance to bad rubbish,' said Biggy, squaring up her shoulders and looking like the avenging queen.

So we all turned and stared at Biggy instead. We'd never seen anything like it. Deepa stifled a giggle. Dhruv threw down his fork and turned his head between the door and Biggy and back again as if he was watching tennis. Preity and I just looked at each other. Anju hid behind her hand.

'I'll go,' I said, standing up.

'Leave her,' said Biggy. 'She's a bad girl. She doesn't deserve any dinner.'

'Mum, that's not fair,' said Anju gently.

'I'll go, Pinky,' said Raj. 'Sit down and eat. She'll forget in a minute.'

But Biggy had already forgotten and was munching away on vegetable biryani as if she hadn't eaten for weeks.

121

Mum wouldn't come back in. She sat in the car and sobbed and wouldn't be consoled. Both their dinners went cold on the plate.

I decided the best thing I could do about the whole situation was help my mum, be there for her when she needed support whether it was practical or emotional. It meant always being available to talk things through. It meant not arguing any more than was necessary, which wasn't easy. It included helping even when I didn't think she was doing the best thing or the right thing or the thing I considered necessary. In other words, care homes kind of got forgotten and health checks became the in thing.

Humour is a fantastically misunderstood defence mechanism. Sometimes you can't help but laugh. It's too painful to confront anything else. Just because people are smiling doesn't mean they aren't breaking inside. People have to make light of situations or they wouldn't survive. But the rebound guilt keeps us up at night. I know that now more than ever.

Chapter 10

It seemed Big Mama had pains in her chest, an extension of those breathless episodes on the phone and probably due to anxiety of some kind. We got her a heart scan, some blood tests, checked her thyroid function and anything else we or the GP could think of. Everything was pretty much fine, exactly what you'd expect in an octogenarian's body. But the chest pains continued.

The next thing was a mammogram. This was entirely Mum's idea as my patience and tact were already wearing thin. But I had agreed with myself to support her so that's what I did.

Off we went to the mammogram clinic and immediately afterwards to Pizza Hut, this time in Nelson Mandela Square just around the corner where there was no danger of meeting a gang of old biddies from the temple. Biggy's boobs appeared to be healthy so in my opinion we had something to celebrate, if only the fact that the whole rigmarole was over.

'I'm worried, Pinky,' said my mum, a forkful of pizza base and roast peppers hovering in front of her.

'What about?' I said, knowing I wasn't going to like what came next.

'If it's not her breasts, what is it?' she said. 'I think we need a full body MRI.'

I nearly choked.

'This is a fucking joke,' I spluttered.

'Don't swear,' she said. 'You're swearing again.'

'Don't fucking swear?' I said.

'Now you're getting hysterical,' she said, panic in her eyes. 'Keep your voice down. I don't know why you have to get so excited about everything.'

'Hysterical?' I said. 'Excited?'

'Just leave it, Pinky,' she said. 'We'll talk about it later.'

'No, we'll talk about it now. We've done all the tests we're going to do. It could have been just a simple thyroid problem, or a heart problem or any those things, but it's not. We've checked every nook and cranny of that woman's body. She's fit and she's healthy. She has dementia. Are you listening? She has dementia.'

The Pizza Hut waitress was hanging about close by, maybe to catch plates if I threw them.

'No, darling, she doesn't,' said Mum, glancing round. 'Be quiet. This is my mother we're talking about and we'll do it my way. I'll talk to the doctor this afternoon and arrange the MRI. I'm going to get to the bottom of this if it kills me.'

'Which it probably will.'

'You sound like you hope so.'

'Well, who could blame me? You just won't bloody listen. It's wrong what you're doing. Wrong. Harassing an elderly lady with all these tests and procedures when everyone can see what it really is.'

'Don't you dare …'

'It's DEMENTIA!' I yelled.

Mum gasped and wrapped her arms around herself, put her head down into her chest.

I covered my mouth with my hands and looked at her in

124

horror as she cried. The restaurant had gone strangely quiet. The waitress appeared at my elbow.

'Is everything ok?' she said, in a small sweet voice.

I realised I was breathing heavily as if I'd just run a marathon.

'Yes,' I managed at last. 'Yes. Sorry. We're just a bit upset, both of us. Sorry.'

She smiled understandingly and offered to clear our plates.

'No, we're not finished,' I said. Then I stood up and spoke to the rest of the diners. 'Sorry, folks. Sorry about that. I hope we haven't spoiled your lunch.'

Then I sat back down and reached across the table for Mum's hand. She looked up at me through her hair with tears down her cheeks, her other hand over her mouth as if to stop anything getting out. She spoke into this hand.

'I can't hear you, Mum,' I said, sniffing back my own tears.

'I said I'm doing the best I can,' she said. 'It's just that according to that book you left on the table, we need to … '

'You have to stop doing that, reading the books, looking stuff up. You'd have to be a proper medic to understand it all and get the bigger picture. That's what GPs are for. That's what I'm for, and Deepa.'

'But it said that a lack of Vitamin D can sometimes make people forgetful. It isn't always sunny in Glasgow and maybe she has a deficiency of sunlight. And chapattis don't have vitamin D – the Readers Digest said that. She eats a lot of chapattis.' She batted her tears away with her free hand.

'Ok. Mum. She doesn't fit that clinical picture. She eats a good diet, her bones are fine and memory loss is end stage,' I said.

'I know all that. I can read and I do have some experience, you know? I've been a nurse all my life. I work with elderly people. It's not just you and Deepa who know about medicine. The next thing is an MRI and if that's clear then …'

'No, Mum,' I said, trying to control my voice, trying not to swear. Failing. 'I don't know why that fucking GP keeps agreeing to all this, whether she's being a bloody pushover or you're just extremely persuasive, or whether she really doesn't have the faintest idea what she's doing. It's amazing.'

'The GP knows exactly what she's doing,' said Mum. 'It's just she's a bit slow to act sometimes. She doesn't know Biggy like I do.'

'I know Biggy pretty well myself,' I said. 'She's my Gran, you know. I've known her all my life.' This was getting childish. I shook my head before going on. 'I'm a doctor, Mum, and you shouldn't be dipping into books like that and picking out bits of information.'

She let go of my hand, wiped her eyes and stuck her nose in the air.

'Please, mum. What other tests does she have to endure?' I said.

She ignored me.

'This is stupid,' I said. 'You're being stupid. Stop behaving like a child and listen to me. I'm a doctor. Why don't you ever listen to me? Big Mama is healthy in everything but her brain which is decaying slowly and …'

'How dare you!' she said suddenly, quiet but fierce. 'This is my mother we're talking about and you have no right.' On she went, telling me off for never visiting Biggy, for thinking I knew everything, for, well, there's no need to elaborate. She was stressed, upset, exhausted and in complete despair over Big Mama. I can say this with hindsight but at the time I was just massively frustrated. She'd done what I'd done when I was a student: every illness I'd heard about at university, I found a family member it would fit. Every illness she read about, she applied to Biggy, saw all the signs and was convinced this latest thing was the problem. I tried explaining this to her, but she wouldn't accept it.

'Deepa's on the front line,' I said. 'You have to listen to Deepa at least.' Deepa had obeyed every request from Biggy and my mum to listen to her chest, take her pulse, check her eyes and her hearing, examine her skin, her nose, her mouth, her feet, and all the other things that had cropped up along the way.

'I don't have to listen to anybody. I can see with my own eyes.'

The waitress came with the coffee. I stirred extra sugar into mine for strength and took a deep breath.

'Mum,' I said in my voice that means I mean business, 'I'm going to tell you something. I'm going to tell you about dementia. No, you have to listen, just this once, and then I'll shut up. I'm going to tell you what the signs are, what the prognosis is, what kind of behaviour we can expect and all the other stuff. When I'm finished you can tell me to get lost and I'll keep my trap shut on the subject forever.'

She glared at me over the cappuccino foam then set the cup down and licked the froth off her spoon. She pulled her lips in tight, her agreement to hear me out without interrupting and

127

arguing back. I kept my voice down, quiet and controlled but absolutely clear so I would know that she hadn't missed a word. I pointed out all the checks we'd done and how healthy Big Mama really was for her age after a life of no alcohol, no meat (apart from the occasional pepperoni) and applied spiritual practice. I told her all the aspects of dementia, what it does to a person, what we could expect, what Biggy would need and why. Every so often she'd open her mouth to butt in but I kept going until it was all out.

'I'm convinced of this now,' I said. The truth was that, having spelled it all out for her, I was even more convinced myself, but also more aware of the tragedy of it all. 'I'm sorry, but this is what I think it is.'

She blinked across at me like a rabbit in the headlights.

'Dementia seems to be the only thing you haven't read up about.'

I wished I hadn't said it. It stung like a wasp, I could see. The pain flashed across her face as if I'd reached over and slapped her. She looked away. I waited for her to answer while she blinked as if she was standing in a hurricane.

'I just don't believe it,' she said, not meeting my gaze. 'It's not true. I can't believe it.'

I glared at her, willing her to turn back to me, but she sat, hunched and staring at the floor, her head drooping slowly onto her chest again until I couldn't bear it anymore and called the waitress for the bill.

We walked back to the car in silence. The only words which passed between us being at the car park pay machine while we searched for change, but at least talking about small change meant the ice was broken.

'You'll never guess what happened yesterday when Anju Masi was visiting Big Mama,' she said, as we left the car park.

'Go on then, tell me,' I said, trying to sound cheerful.

'Well, you know how sometimes Biggy gets confused about who's who?'

'Yes …' I said, not keen on this story.

'We were just having a cup of tea and Anju had made cakes, when Biggy asked her where Baby was. You know how she sometimes calls Anju 'Baby'. It was her pet name for her when we were younger, because she's the youngest. Rather than point out to Biggy that Baby was sitting right there in front of her, Anju just told her that Baby was at home. So Biggy asked her where her husband, Yogi Uncle, was. So Anju says, 'He's at home with Baby.' At which point Biggy started exclaiming 'That's terrible! So he has two wives now? He's a terrible man to have two wives. You'll have to go home straight away and sort this out. He's your husband. You have to tell Baby that." I was negotiating a particularly tricky junction at this point but I glanced over at her. She was laughing her head off but her eyes were still wet. 'Wasn't that just so funny?' she said.

And I thought 'Yes, I suppose it is,' and I started laughing too. Because you've got to laugh, haven't you? So we spent the rest of the journey revisiting all the stories about the crazy things Big Mama had done. And I didn't mention dementia again, not to her. She had to get there in her own sweet time.

It wasn't long after that we went for that Mothers Day meal,

129

in Chillies again. You can see how the rest of us were getting tired of the same restaurant, but at least the staff were used to our little ways. This was the meal where I asked Biggy the Billy Connolly question:

'Bill Connolly Kee khenda? What does Billy Connolly say?' I said.

And Biggy stared at me blankly, her face brassing up. 'I don't know,' she said. 'You tell me what Billy Connolly says.'

The 'You tell me' game was one of her tricks to cover her forgetfulness. Then when you tell her the answer, in this case 'Bloody Fucking!' she says 'I knew that. Of course, I knew that.'

But we all saw that happen. We knew there was no denying it anymore. This was the proof we'd all needed, those of us who hadn't believed before. I realised that in some tiny way I had still hoped it wasn't true myself but could no longer avoid it either. It was dementia, it wasn't going to get better, and it wasn't just a passing illness. She was leaving us and had, for the most part, already gone. She was like an empty vessel, there but not there, or like a photograph of the life that was once in her but wasn't there anymore. There were still bits and pieces of that life, glimpses of the person she once was, the tower of strength and wisdom, the long-established ways of living, but the reality was she was regressing more and more into an increasingly infantile position.

After the Mother's Day meal, I texted everyone, everyone that is, except my mum. 'What the fuck was that? What are we going to do?' I wrote. Ages later Anju Masi phoned.

'What do you mean?' she said. 'There's nothing to be done.'

Argh!

I missed Deepa who hadn't been at the meal because she was working in Manchester. She'd have understood. She'd have known what to do, but she must have been doing one of her seventy hour weeks. Dhruv texted that he was busy and he'd phone later. Finally Raj called.

'This is worse than I'd realised,' I said. 'I've never seen her like that.'

'What is it?'

'Dementia,' I said, hating the sound of it.

'Is it?' he said. 'What exactly does that mean?' A lawyer, not a doctor, he had the sense to defer to my medical knowledge. I told him much of what I'd said to my mum that day in Pizza Hut.

'I don't believe it had to be like this,' I said. 'If she'd used her brain a wee bit more she wouldn't be in this position.'

'That's what I thought,' he said.

'Really?' What a relief to hear him say it! I thought he'd be ticked off with me for being so heartless.

'Yeah,' he said. 'Of course. If she'd learnt more than just basic English, if she'd got a job ...'

'If she'd read a book, instead of all that knitting!'

'Gone to a night class, learnt a skill.'

'Mum and Anju Masi should have taught her to drive, got her a bit of independence, pushed her more.'

'It's so irresponsible!'

What were we like?

'So,' he said, 'what are we going to do?'

'Call Preity. Call Dhruv. Talk.'

So we met for a coffee and swapped horror stories and shared

131

how much we hated going to visit, how hard it was to keep a conversation going, how pissed off with her we all were. We agreed it was shameful to feel the way we did about our own Gran who had done so much for us, but we all shared the experienced the same block when it came to visiting. Only Deepa, living in Manchester, so lovely and easy when she came back, couldn't understand our confusion. We decided we had to try harder and to offer ourselves and our time to my mum and Anju Masi. If we couldn't do it for Biggy, we had to do it for Mum and Anju.

More family meetings were called. We argued occasionally about care homes, but I knew it was really a nursing home she'd need. Raj looked online and came up with the only nursing home that spoke Punjabi and supplied genuine Indian food. It was in London. He phoned my mum.

'London?' she said. 'I don't want to send her away to London! Is this what it's come to? I can't. I just can't!' And she burst into tears.

Thanks, Raj.

I started going in on a Monday during my lunch-time, but the first time I went, Mum was there.

'What are you doing here?' I said. 'The whole point is to give you a break.'

'I'm only round the corner anyway,' she said. 'I just wanted to make sure you managed.'

This kind of thing kept happening. Every time any of us arranged to do something to help, either Anju Masi or my mum would show up too.

'Of course I'm alright,' I said. 'We need to feel needed too, us kids. You have to let us do this.'

But it must have been hard to let go of being necessary twenty-four hours a day, and Mum and Anju were such a tight twosome. For a while there seemed to be no room for the rest of us.

We made Big Mama a photo book, putting photos on her phone instead of names and numbers. We gave her a special whiteboard with the day of the week and the date and what was happening that day, and we changed it religiously every time we visited. She got our names mixed up, got our faces mixed up, worried about us for all the wrong reasons because she thought we were younger than we were, or occasionally forgot our names altogether.

Then, at last, we got the diagnosis. Big Mama has the Alzheimer's form of dementia. I felt like I could breathe again, but also couldn't. It was a relief but a jump into the start of another journey. As a term, dementia was a bit of a poisoned chalice because none of us really understood what it meant. At last we had a name for what was going on but not knowing what that meant in a practical sense sparked another long sharing of opinions from the family. For many the term reeked of stigma. There was a mixture of bewilderment, relief, denial and hopelessness but, most of all, finality. It's hard to say now, looking back who experienced which of these emotions because I think we all went through every one of them at different times.

My generation, were probably more up to speed with accepting it than the others, but for a long time the older ones looked for signs that she was getting better and in many ways I suspect they still do. For myself, I went between giving up completely and thinking that there was no point in accepting it, painfully aware that she is still a real person, the real Big Mama, underneath the diagnosis.

We all got together and made a plan.

Then we made another plan.

And another.

As a family we're quite good at making plans. Just not so good at making them happen. But while we were busy making plans, life just kept on happening.

Enter the next disaster.

My mum was worried about what Big Mama got up to at night and first thing in the morning, because she always seemed tired even though she went to bed really early. So at the end of a twelve hour shift (which finished at midnight) she texted Anju Masi that she was going up to Big Mama's to stay and keep an eye on her.

'What are you doing that for?' Anju texted back. 'You don't need to go. She'll only chase you away. You'll get no sleep. Just go home and I'll come in the morning.' This is the shortened version. You know how sisters can argue.

'I'm at Mum's and I'm staying,' was Mum's final text, even though she hadn't left work, then she switched off the phone.

Biggy didn't know she was coming and was already in bed. There was a blanket on the famous blue leather sofa in the sitting room, so she crawled under it and dozed off. Biggy got up a couple of times to the toilet then went back to bed: nothing unusual there. Then at six o'clock she came into the living room, put on the light and saw my Mum lying there. She didn't say a word, but started cleaning like a woman possessed. She had a mop and was wielding it as if the Goddess Lakshmi was on her way over.

'Mum,' said my mum. 'I'm here. It's six o'clock in the morning. Why don't you go back to bed and we'll get up later and I'll help you clean the house?'

'It's ok,' said Biggy without pausing. 'You just go back to sleep. I'll be finished in a minute.'

Mum was scared. Biggy's eyes were glazed and she was like a mad woman, 'pagal' as Big Mama would call it, scrubbing and rubbing so furiously as if she was cleaning out an evil spirit. She almost didn't seem to know what she was doing. Mum kept still and hoped she'd finish the living room and go back to bed.

She did finish the living room then went down the hall to the bathroom.

Mum listened for the flush and the sound of her going to bed. But instead there was an almighty crash. She ran to the bathroom. Biggy was lying on her back with the mop handle bent underneath her and her leg sticking out at a weird angle.

Families should be there for each other, through the good, the bad and everything else in between – the mundane, the hopeless and the unknown. In our case, a little bit of knowledge goes a very long way. Sometimes it goes too far. We like to discuss, we like to include everyone – almost to the point where people get lost. Did

Biggy get lost? Did we take too long? Did we do the right things, say the right things? We couldn't see the wood for the trees, or we were too busy looking at a single tree to notice the others falling around us. Egos took over; words became more important than actions. But it takes strength and it takes courage to admit you were wrong and not to gloat when you are right. Dementia isn't about right or wrong. It's about support, strength and caring enough to walk with the person no matter what. Sometimes you are too tired though. What happens if you can't go on? Who helps then?

Rita and Biggy

Chapter 11

If it weren't for the mop, Big Mama's fall might never have happened, but if it weren't for the mop it might have been much, much worse. We think what happened is that she leant on it, and being only plastic it buckled under her weight. Biggy can't remember, so she can't tell us. But her head missed the sink by millimetres.

'My God, what's happened?' said Mum.

'Help me! Get me up!' shouted Biggy.

'Let me see you first,' said Mum, knowing, as a nurse, what not to do.

Biggy was screaming in pain. 'Get me up! How could you be so heartless? I want to get up!'

Mum had a quick look and realised there was a good chance something was broken. One leg was stretched out but the other one was bent. Mum could see that the ankle was twisted at a right angle to her body.

Biggy kept saying 'Straighten my leg!'

'No, Mum, I can't move it.' She got round the back of her and tried to ease her up. If it had only been a strain then she could have born her own weight and been able to stand up, but she couldn't so Mum had to lay her back down again. 'I can't, Mum,' she said as calmly as she could. 'It might cause more damage.'

'What do you mean? Just get me up off this floor! Now! What a daughter!'

'Really, I can't. It might be broken. Shall we try and sit you up?'

'Bad daughter! How could you leave your mother on the floor?'

She screamed in pain as Mum tried to get her to up into a sitting position. Mum laid her back down as gently as she could, shaking all the time herself. She knew now the foot was completely rotated that she should not be moving her at all.

She went for a pillow and a blanket.

'Listen to me, Mum,' she said. 'As a nurse I'm telling you there's no way I can move you. Let's get your head onto this pillow.'

'I don't want a pillow. I want to get up! I just want to go and sit on the sofa. I'd be fine if you'd just lift me. What kind of daughter are you?'

'There, that's better, isn't it?'

'I don't want to lay here. I don't want a blanket. I'm hot. Far too hot. Get me out of this corner.'

'I can't. Will you listen to me? Something might be broken. I'm going to phone for an ambulance.'

She ran through to the phone and left Biggy screaming in pain, demanding to be lifted and hurling the most unbelievable abuse at her, lots of bloodys and fuckings.

'Just leave me here to die then!' she screamed.

Mum dialled 999 and got through immediately. She explained the situation as calmly as she could. This is where nursing training helps, obviously. She was able to explain exactly what she saw and what she thought had happened. But Biggy is her mother so I can only imagine how scary the whole thing must have been. It's different when it's your own family.

'It'll be about an hour or so,' said the person on the phone.

'An hour?' said Mum, incredulous. 'Are you kidding? This is an eighty year old lady who has fallen and is in excruciating pain. Can you hear her?' She held the phone in the direction of the bathroom. 'You need to come quicker than that. She's stuck on the bathroom floor with her leg at right angles.'

'Yes, but the information you've given me is she's breathing, she's conscious. It's not a cardiac arrest. This is not an emergency. Just keep her comfortable. We'll be there as soon as we can.'

A cold sweat ran through my mum. An hour? Really? Are you serious?

She went back through and crouched on the floor beside Biggy trying to comfort her, but there was no calming her down.

'Get me up!'

'I can't move you. The moment I do, that leg's going to snap. It would be wrong of me to do anything. They'll be here soon.' She didn't tell her they'd said an hour.

Thankfully the ambulance actually arrived less than twenty minutes later, but it felt like an eternity to my mum. Biggy never let up, never calmed down, never took any of the comfort offered, but the pain she must have been in would have been extraordinary, even though Biggy has always had a very high pain threshold. Mum's still embarrassed about them arguing because it carried on all the way to the hospital and in the hospital. It was still happening when I arrived. But it wasn't an argument really.

140

It was just a desperate situation. As well as being in a lot of pain, Biggy would have been in shock and so too would my mum have been. In the past, Biggy would never have argued with anyone in any circumstance but the dementia can cause even the most placid person to be aggressive.

The paramedics gave her gas and air to numb the pain. They knew immediately that the leg was broken so they didn't move her straight away either. Instead they got a scoop chair and lifted her into that, carried her downstairs and onto the stretcher. They took her to Accident and Emergency where she was assessed, x-rayed and given the diagnosis. Her hip was broken, the femur and yes, her whole leg was out at right angles to her body. She would need an operation later that day.

That this happened at six in the morning is unusual. Biggy was never an early bird. But what was also weird was the fact that Mum didn't tell anyone until after nine. I got a text message from her, nonchalant as always. All her texts are very matter-of-fact. Perhaps this comes from Mum's early belief that you paid for text messages by the letter.

'Big mama in hospital. Fractured hip. Its fine. Don't bother coming.'

'What the fuck are you talking about?! Don't be so bloody stupid. Of course I'm coming.'

'I didn't want to bother anyone,' she said later. 'What difference would it have made? There was nothing anyone could do.'

Obviously I went straight up. Anju Masi was right behind me.

'This is exactly what we're supposed to be there for,' I said.

So I saw this leg of Biggy's still sticking right out the wrong way. I texted everybody but couldn't get hold of Deepa who was probably working. I put it on Facebook hoping some of my medical friends might have some advice. 'Get them to put a block in,' they all said, by which time the anaesthetist had been round and done just that. This is an injection given at the site of pain which numbs the nerves supplying the area.

Despite such severe pain, Big Mama was still arguing with my mum.

'Why are you not taking me off this chair? Why are you not taking me home? Where am I?' she asked.

And Mum was asking her questions too: 'What day is it?'

This may seem strange, but Mum thought Biggy might be in a state of shock, which she was, and asking someone what day it is can be a good way to ascertain whether they are or not. The fact that Biggy already didn't know what day it was most of the time was neither here nor there.

Mum looked dreadful. She looked so bad I couldn't help thinking she ought to be in the bed next door. By eleven in the morning Biggy had been transferred to the ward upstairs, a similar one in the same building to the one my dad had been in all those years earlier.

'You've been here for ages,' said one of the nurses. 'Why don't you take a wee break?'

'Yeah, come on, Mum,' I said. 'They need to get her settled into the side room in the ward. It's nearly lunch-time. We can go and eat.' So me, Mum and Anju went to the University Café, an old Italian café nearby in Glasgow's West End.

During the time we were away, Biggy fell twice. Forgetting completely that she had fallen in her own bathroom or been in an ambulance or been examined by a variety of medics or been in extreme pain, she had done the obvious thing, which was to try and get up. She didn't understand where she was or what she was doing there, so she shimmied past the side gates on her bed, designed to keep her from falling out, until she was at the bottom of the bed, then slid off onto the floor. Of course she had no idea that her legs couldn't hold her, o as soon as she tried to bear her own weight she landed in a heap on the floor. One of these times she was caught by a nurse, but the other time she wasn't. This is the dilemma of side rooms. In the old days there would have been a huge ward with a nurses' station either in the middle or at one end. There would have been no privacy whatsoever but at least she would have been watched. The new idea of side rooms is for infection control and privacy and for acutely unwell patients. This was a surgical ward so they didn't have the capacity for the one-to-one she needed and they didn't fully comprehend her dementia either or the difference that it makes.

I've actually seen lots of elderly people do what Biggy did, and so has my mum. They just clamber over the cot-sides or go down to the end of the bed and slide out as Big Mama did. It's incredible to watch, as long as no-one gets hurt, but not when it's your own relative doing it.

She fell five times in total and was in hospital for only four days. Three of those times were pre-operation, the other two afterwards.

She was, of course, very agitated, although on the first day she was actually remarkably good. Her leg was still numb I suppose, but after the operation and the pain killers had worn off, she was up shouting and screaming, wanting to go home. They couldn't control her so they had her sitting right in the middle of the room where they could see her. When we visited the next day they said they needed somebody who could stay with her twenty-four hours because they just didn't have the staff. The relatives had to do it, or in this case Mum and Anju.

This seemed quite unfair. They were both working full-time then going into hospital and essentially doing night-shifts. There's nowhere in these side rooms for extra people to sleep. By the end of it they were completely and utterly exhausted.

Even though Big Mama had no concentration, it still seemed a shame that there was no TV in the side room, nothing to distract her – no visitors, no ward staff, nothing. It's no wonder she was especially agitated.

After a couple of nights of this it was Raj's graduation. He said he couldn't go to his own graduation, not without Biggy or Mum.

'Can one of you stay here?' the nurses wanted to know.

So to be fair Mum and Anju Masi said they'd both stay.

'No, Mum,' we said. 'Raj needs you to go and you need to go for yourself too. He's your son.'

So Anju stayed and Mum went. We've got family photos of the graduation, not formal ones, because as soon as the graduation ceremony was over Raj went straight to the hospital to have his photos taken in the Western with Biggy and Anju too. The certificate got passed around as usual as if nothing had happened. Biggy wasn't standing, of course. She was still in the

144

seat at that point. But it was a lovely moment.

Big Mama got shifted four times during her three day stay in the general hospital. Think about that, for somebody with dementia who, because of her illness, finds even small changes quite disorientating and therefore upsetting. At one point she was shifted into another side room further up the ward and while she was alone in there the ceiling collapsed. This was absolutely terrifying for her. It missed her by a few centimetres and she quite understandably started screaming again. They had to move her again, this time into a four-bedded ward. Even within that ward she was moved three times. None of this helped her confusion. To cap it all, after three days she was moved to another hospital. Finally she was moved to a long-stay unit.

The long-stay unit was essentially a nursing home. Similar problems arose there too. Initially she was in a side room again, but then moved to a 'bay' type of area with other patients in a larger room, about six other people in total. This was all right because she could watch what was going on around her and the staff could keep an eye on her too. She was there until just before Christmas, until the last move.

There were far too many moves – too many moves and too many different people looking after her. Sometimes it was even men who were looking after her most personal needs, which really distressed her. Plus she couldn't understand the concept of the buzzer or the idea of having to buzz when she needed help, never mind being able to recognise when she needed that help in the first place. There was a language problem too. And of course she was still in a lot of very serious pain.

Mum had various arguments with the staff about the pain management. When she was in recovery she was prescribed a strong morphine-based pain-killer. It was written in her notes: 'as and when' she needed it. But Biggy was not in a position to ask for it, she didn't have the mental capacity. Mum asked the doctor repeatedly to put her onto something regular so that she'd be more in control of the pain, which eventually the doctor did. Because my mum was there the whole day she could assess her needs more easily. The nurses never came near her. They were massively overstretched. The whole system's overstretched. It was a constant struggle.

The physiotherapist came and helped her to walk and she was in a lot of pain. Mum asked the physio if she thought Biggy needed a stronger pain-killer.

'Yes, I can see she's really sore,' the physio said.

Mum went to the nurses and there was another argument. Sometimes I think the more you ask for help for your relative, the less you're going to get. That's human nature. It's not whether it's fair or unfair. Personally I think it's futile to enter into arguments with medical staff which is why I haven't but it's what my mum tends to do. It's easier for her to understand it through her nursing than to get too personal about it. Your capacity to care as a daughter or a Granddaughter becomes stretched anyway. She wants to do what's best for Big Mama, but because she knows the ward, it's hard not to want to dictate what happens there.

If you ask Mum she won't say that she's exhausted. She won't say 'I was tired' or 'I was losing my patience' or 'It was just getting too much for me.' She doesn't know when to stop, but then stopping can be a hard thing to do in these circumstances. She didn't want us there that first day. She wanted to deal with it all herself. Mum always works herself into the ground.

'I'll handle it,' she'll say. 'That's just me. I'm a perfectionist. If you're going to do a job you need to do it well.'

That's what always happens in our family. One person decides they're taking on whatever it is so the rest of us don't need to do it and inevitably what happens is everybody turns up. Only Preity didn't come that day. Unusually, she said 'I'll just stay at home. Text me what happens.' Deepa was obviously in Manchester and the boys were on the periphery anyway, but Anju and I got there.

Mum still feels guilty about the fall – as if it was her fault or that she should have known. I had been warning her something was going to happen but she couldn't hear it. She didn't want it to be true. I wish it hadn't been.

The fall happened at the beginning of October and within a week Big Mama was in long-term nursing care. There had been no family discussion. Bala Masi had not been summoned. The decision had been taken out of our hands. But Mum persisted.

'Do you think she'll be home for Christmas?' she asked me one day, not long after Biggy had arrived in the long stay unit.

'No, Mum, I don't think she'll be home for Christmas,' I said. 'I don't think she's coming home.'

'Let's just wait and see what happens, eh?' she said. 'Maybe she'll be back in her own place by Christmas.'

'For fuck's sake!' I thought, but didn't say. So I decided I had to be direct and cold-hearted about it. I said 'If you think she is going to get back to her own home you can forget about it. We, as in Preity and I, are not letting her go back home. It's not safe.'

We all have different roles in this family. Mine often seems to be to deliver bad news. Mum was looking at it from a hopeful point of view. We saw it differently because we were less involved on a day to day basis. We were both worried about our mums. What was needed was a new plan …

My mum wanted to retire and have Biggy come and stay with her, but the rest of us knew this would only lead to disaster because Biggy's dementia was only going to get worse.

Families dealing with dementia often have to balance optimism with realism and this can be difficult to comprehend. Especially in a family that prides itself on fighting and never giving up. It is hard when you don't have control anymore, when the decision is taken out of your hands. For Big Mama, her mind was losing control, but for my mum the control was being taken away from her. Doing what is best in the long run can often feel like the biggest paradox, but giving in isn't necessarily defeat. Acceptance sometimes calms things down in order to let us all move forwards.

Chapter 12

Big Mama developed some new habits while she was in the unit. Mum went in one day wearing a fancy designer scarf that Anju had given her for Christmas. There was a neat pile of clothes sitting on Big Mama's bed and Biggy was sitting in the chair beside it.

'Give me your scarf,' said Biggy.

'Why do you want my scarf? It's roasting in here,' said Mum.

'I need it to tie up my clothes so I can take them home,' said Biggy.

Rather than argue outright, Mum obliged and watched her wrap the beautiful scarf round the clothes. Then they set off down the corridor, Mum holding the bundle and Biggy with her Zimmer. She still wasn't able to walk unaided.

Another time Raj and I arrived to find her walking down the corridor with her belongings wrapped in some kind of red rug and hanging off the Zimmer. It reminded me of those pictures in kids' story books of little lost orphans travelling the world with a bundle on the end of a stick, always a red bundle. Other times she'd fill her pillow case and take that, or her dressing gown would be open on the bed and piled with stuff which she'd then wrap and tie together with the cord. And on one memorable occasion she had the whole lot secured with a pair of giant knickers. She was very inventive. She knew what she was doing.

'Stop laughing at me!' she said.

It was difficult not to see the funny side, but it was also tragic. She just wanted to go home.

But this was not to be. We had already looked at some nursing homes, as you'll remember, as one of our previous plans. But finally our hand had been forced by the fall and her new physical needs.

'We need to get Bala Masi over from Canada for another discussion,' said Mum.

'Why?' I said. 'It won't change anything. We don't have a choice anymore.'

'This is a major decision. You can't just decide to put her into a nursing home. If it was one of my own patients I'd go and speak to the relatives and advise them to go home and discuss their Gran's future as a family, to consider ... '

'She's not safe in her own home and it would be too much for you to look after her in yours.'

'No, it wouldn't,' she said. 'I'd manage.'

So I reminded her of when my dad was dying. He was in the hospital and we had left the refuge and gone back to the house in Bearsden. I had said 'Why can't we just take him home?' I reminded her of what her reply had been.

'You said to me, quite rightly, 'No, there are nurses, Macmillan nurses, for that. He's in the hospice and he's in the right place.' Because I'd said to you I didn't want him to die out there in the hospital but you said that actually it would have been cruel of us to have him sitting there in our house not getting the care and medical attention he needed.'

'This is completely different.'

I disagreed. Dad had multi-organ failure, but Biggy's brain is an organ too, and it's failing. This is the distinction between dementia and a physical illness. Because it's her brain and therefore her mind and her personality that are affected, we somehow think that we can make her be OK again. Because it's the person she is that we're losing, not a limb.

'That's so difficult to deal with, isn't it, Mum?'

So Bala Masi came from Canada. She went to visit Big Mama and they decided to take her to the coffee shop along the corridor. Mum, relieved to have Bala there and be able to take a back seat, hung behind and let Biggy and Bala walk together and talk.

'Do you know about such and such a thing?' said Big Mama. My mum couldn't quite make out what the such and such was.

'No, I don't know about that,' said Bala Masi.

There was a little pause.

'What are you talking about?' said Big Mama.

'I don't know what you're talking about,' said Bala Masi. 'What *are* you talking about?'

It was Mum's turn to laugh. They were as bad as each other.

'I don't know. What are you talking about?' said Big Mama.

But then there was the time she stole the other lady's chocolate. That was just embarrassing.

Walking down the same corridor with my mum one day, she passed this other patient who was carrying a load of chocolate bars her daughter had brought in for her. Biggy grabbed one as she went past saying 'That's mine!' and took off round the corner as fast as her broken hip and Zimmer would allow. Mum was

151

mortified and had to go and buy a load more chocolate to replace it.

So Bala Masi had arrived for yet another discussion. One of other difficulties we had was that putting your relative into a home is not the accepted thing in Asian families. It felt fundamentally wrong to my mum, Anju and Bala. It would have felt wrong to Biggy too if she'd been aware of what was going on. So Mum came up with all sorts of schemes. As well as retiring early she was going to sell the house and move somewhere small enough for just her and Big Mama. Or she'd move into the nursing home with her if she had to – lots of carefully worked out plans, none of which would work. She didn't want her mum to feel like she had been abandoned. But my poor mum was a lone voice. We all told her over and over again: 'You can't do this. She needs twenty-four hour nursing care.' Fortunately Bala and Anju were more or less in agreement about this. It was very hard for Mum to let go.

In the end it all came down to funding and where a bed was available. A vacancy came up in a home nearer to Anju Masi quicker than it did in Glasgow and, therefore, another big debate.

'Maybe we should find somewhere in between?' someone said.

Argh!

There were also new residential homes being built in Bearsden, even closer to my mum. Unfortunately they didn't take dementia patients.

'Even if they took Biggy, Mum would never be out of there,' said all the kids, Anju Masi and everybody else.

152

She'd have taken her for the day and brought her home or gone up there herself and spent the whole day with Big Mama. She doesn't see that this is wrong. If Biggy was in her own home, none of us would ever stay longer than thirty or forty five minutes. She gets twitchy after that and you run out of things to talk about. Biggy may have dementia but she still has her concept of personal space. She likes being on her own, demented or not.

As well as the big family meetings there's always something that gets said on top, and then I get told or Deepa gets told and then it comes back to Mum or Anju. That's the way our family is.

'Where did you hear that?' they'll say. 'That was an off-the-cuff remark when I sat down for my dinner. Why didn't you come and speak to me about it?'

'I didn't want to hurt your feelings,' we all say.

It's like Chinese whispers.

Preity will phone me. 'My mum's on the phone to your mum just now. I'm monitoring the conversation. I'll text you back and let you know what she said.' Oh dear.

I've seen Mum and Anju Masi, and of course Bala Masi and Nani Maa too, all go through the full the range of emotions over this. The new nursing home was a lovely complex with beautiful views and the full range of care. There were many advantages to it. It was the best option we had.

'No-one speaks her language,' said Mum.

'There's no Indian food,' said Anju.

'She won't be able to go to the temple,' said Mum.

'She doesn't go any more anyway,' I said.

'She won't be able to walk down to the shops,' said Mum.

153

'She doesn't nowadays,' said Preity. 'Hasn't for ages.'

'I'm abandoning my own mother!' said Mum.

'I don't want to see her suffer any more and go through this dementia,' said Anju Masi. 'I wish God would just take her. It's a terrible thing to wish but I can't bear her suffering. If she'd died in that fall, she wouldn't have had to go through all this...'

There seemed to be guilt for Mum and Anju Masi every way they turned.

'I personally feel we are holding her a prisoner in there,' said Anju. 'She wants to get out and we won't let her.'

'Every day when we leave her, the way she is becomes reflected in our mood when we come home,' observed Mum.

It wasn't just stressful for Mum but also for the whole family. Luckily we are a strong family and while we may argue and discuss and disagree and fight over every little point, we never actually fall out. There's never a time someone says, 'That's it. We're through. I'm never talking to you again.' I think we're very lucky in this. I know of other families who have broken apart completely.

It was decided. Big Mama, who had no idea important decisions were being made on her behalf, was to move to the nursing home near Anju. It was to happen before Christmas, two days before Christmas to be absolutely exact.

She had no idea where she was going.

The nursing home is a bit like a holiday home. It has extensive grounds and various levels of care. She had a long journey there, which gave it that holiday feel, and then she was given a lovely room with a beautiful view. There was a terrible smell when we arrived, that smell all old people's homes seem to have, like old urine or cabbage. Mum took some plug-ins to combat it so it soon went. Luckily the room was, superficially, quite like her old place in Arlington Street in the sheltered housing complex, so in a way her confusion helped her feel at home. In the beginning when she asked to be taken back to Arlington Street, Mum reminded her about the ceiling falling in at the hospital. This event was traumatic enough for her to remember it but not to remember where it happened.

'But the ceiling fell down in Arlington Street,' Mum would say. 'Unfortunately the whole building had to be demolished. So you can't go back there. But the housing association have given you this place instead. It's nice here, isn't it?'

But she was miserable and so were Mum and Anju Masi. Everyone tried hard to make it work but Christmas was just horrible, indescribably so.

'If she hasn't settled in three months I'm taking her out,' said Mum. It was the only way she could allow it to go on. 'And what I'll do is I'll take her home on my days off.' She works twelve hour shifts on a three week rota, four shifts one week and three the next two. This means she sometimes has gaps of almost a full week during which she thought Biggy could come home.

Meanwhile, she was practically living in the nursing home with Biggy, every day for hours. Big Mama never got a moments peace. The staff never got a moments peace either. Mum never even gave herself a moment's peace.

There's no Indian food in the home, so Anju and my mum make meals for her and take them down. Sometimes they make plenty so they can be frozen and used as needed. The communal part of the complex feels a bit like a day centre so that's where Biggy thinks she is during the day, and then she goes 'home' to her room in the evening. To begin with she continued packing up her things in whatever came to hand and followed us out to the car as if to leave. We had already learnt to be ready with reasons: 'I'm going straight to work,' or 'There's only two seats in my car and Stephen is with me.'

Mum and Anju used to take her out for a meal or somewhere nice for the day or back to Anju's which was close by, but it always ended in trouble. She wouldn't understand why she was being taken back to the home and they'd be heartbroken leaving her.

Once when we went to visit with Nani Maa, Biggy looked terrible. She was grey, like she was when Papa Ji died. She was depressed. Even as a psychiatrist I thought it looked like biological, clinical depression. She had lost her spirit.

'I don't want to talk,' she said.

We gave her food, as she would have done for us.

'I don't want to eat. Just leave me alone. My heart's not in it anymore.'

Nothing seemed to work. Nothing would lift her.

It was a long time before she'd eat with the other residents too.

Then one day Anju Masi phoned.

'Your mum's been down there since nine this morning,' she said. 'It's three o'clock now and your Mum hasn't eaten. She's exhausted but she doesn't seem to want to leave. I've tried everything but she just won't go home.'

Shit! I wondered what could have happened. Mum's visits were usually identical to each other. She'd help Biggy make them both a cup of tea, and then they'd watch some TV. Dinner came at 5pm so Mum would make an excuse to go off for a bit because otherwise Biggy spent the whole time feeding Mum the food instead of eating it herself. Afterwards they'd watch a religious programme if there was one on. (Biggy couldn't watch TV at the very beginning, so this was progress.) Then about 7pm they'd do prayers for half an hour and afterwards Mum would help her get into her night clothes and put her dentures in the glass. Sometimes she'd get ready for bed and sometimes she wouldn't.

'No I'm not tired yet.'

When I got Anju's phone call it was only mid-afternoon, but one of those dark, cold, miserable winter afternoons. I sent Mum a text: 'I'm coming down to drag you out of that nursing home.' But she didn't get it.

I jumped into the car and sped off down there. She was just coming out as I arrived.

'What are you doing here?' she said.

'What are you doing here?' I replied.

'Don't be silly, Pinky.'

'No,' I said. 'Don't you be silly. I'm here to drag you out of this place. I want a word with you.'

We got into her car and I laid it on the line. Why is it always me? I told her in no uncertain terms that she had to stop going down to the home every day. Biggy needed her space. The staff needed their space. Biggy was never going to settle as long as she and Anju were in there all the time. Biggy needed to be left alone to do that.

'Sometimes less is more,' I said. 'You need to give her space to settle. She still knows who you are and she doesn't like being crowded. You wouldn't like it if I was following you about 24/7 watching you.' I was the bossiest thing in Bossyville. I had to be.

'But the staff are not doing their job,' she said, 'they're not letting her settle and they're not giving her medication at exactly the time.'

I said, 'You're a nurse. Just leave it.'

Big Mama had had an aggressive episode. She had tried to take somebody's jewellery or that's what another patient had accused her of doing.

'She's taken my jewellery and she's refusing to take it off and give it back,' said the lady.

So Biggy bit one of the staff and slapped another.

'She needs an anti-psychotic,' I said. 'This is the front part of her brain that is deteriorating.' And I tried to explain the medical side of it.

I left her to think about what I had said as if she was a naughty child. I went back to my fancy red sports car and I watched as she started her own car and drove out of the car park for the hour-long journey home. Incidentally, as soon as she left I found that my fancy red sports car wouldn't start. I found myself phoning her to come back and rescue me!

When I worked in nursing homes myself I used to wonder at the mundane nature of life in a home. There's nothing to do there. No stimulation. Nothing. But I had come to realise that the

158

residents were so consumed with the basics of life that any change was a difficulty not a pleasure. A day out is a hindrance to a peaceful life rather than something fun. What Big Mama needed was a nice routine.

I think Mum heard what I was saying that day. She stopped going every day and didn't stay as long when she did. Gradually she went less and less and now she's only there once or twice a week. Even so Mum is not entirely convinced.

'I still don't think we made the right decision, putting her into a home,' she said. 'She's not happy.'

'She is happy, Mum.'

'I don't think so. I could have easily retired if people had let me.'

'It's not about retiring. You can't easily take care of her.'

'When she fell in the bathroom I thought I could look after her.'

'Surely you know now it wouldn't have been possible? Remember the car door incident?'

'This is not what I wanted.'

The car door incident was probably the thing that clinched it. It was one of those times when Mum had taken her home for a few days. Everything had been absolutely fine. They'd been out for a curry, gone shopping in Clydebank and even gone to her old day centre and met up with friends and talked away. Then Biggy lay down for half an hour and, when she woke, had became completely confused. Unfortunately it was also time to go back. There was no question of staying because her medication had run out.

She became very anxious and agitated and refused to go.

'This is my house,' she shouted in a house that had never been hers. 'Get out of my house.'

After lots more screaming and shouting on Biggy's part and lots of persuasion of various kinds, Mum tried to manhandle her into the car. She eventually got her in, locked the door and raced round to the driver's side, by which time Biggy had unlocked her side and got out. This happened four or five times. Biggy even managed to grab the keys and at one point sat herself down in the middle of the road and refused to move. She was like a petulant child again, but unlike a petulant child you couldn't just scoop her up and carry her off.

'She's abducting me!' she was already shouting. 'Help! She's abusing me! Help me! I want to phone the police.'

Fortunately this didn't last too long. She suddenly got up and walked up the neighbour's path.

'Mum! Where are you going?'

'I want to phone the police and I want to go to the toilet,' said Biggy.

'Right then,' said my poor Mum. 'I'll wait.'

As soon as she came out again, she put her in the car, quickly got back in herself and started driving. But for the whole hour's journey Biggy shouted and abused her, cursing like a trooper the whole time. Mum was terrified she would open the door as they hurtled down the motorway and of Big Mama falling out. It sounded horrendous the way she told it. Big Mama was banging on the window trying to attract the attention of other drivers. But it convinced Mum not to bring her home again.

160

This was also before her medication had really settled down. Getting the medication right can be a case of trial and error because everyone's body chemistry is different. The painkillers for the fall had messed everything up and she wasn't on the right dose, which was causing endless agitation. She'd also been crying for Papa Ji again and occasionally being quite aggressive. We had to call in the Community Psychiatric Nurse and ask for a change. Luckily Yogi Uncle and Anju Masi are pharmacists and also know the area and the home well.

If I told her the kind of stuff she'd said to my mum, Biggy would be horrified. She'd be saying 'How dare you say that I would say that?' She genuinely wouldn't believe that it could have come out of her mouth. Perhaps this is one of the few positive things about dementia, this loss of short-term memory. Unlike many other people of her age, she has no awareness of her friends dying and therefore doesn't suffer endless funerals and the dull ache of repeated bereavements. Instead when we go to visit her she talks a wee bit about Anju Masi and a little bit about Dhruv and Preity, but really all she talks about is us, the whole lot of us and what a wonderful family unit we are. She tells us how fantastic my mum is and how many sacrifices she's made and how hard she works. But like a young mum leaving her toddler crying at the door of the nursery who five minutes later is playing happily with the other kids, Mum worries night after night about the change in Biggy and feels guilty for not going every day. Biggy sleeps soundly, blissfully unaware of saying anything horrible to her at all, while Mum misses her endless phone calls.

As well as that, Mum misses making her own incessant phone

calls to check she's up and dressed or she's ready for the bus to the temple, or whatever would have been happening that day. She doesn't know what to do with her own free time which she suddenly has lots of and spends it pottering about aimlessly, like a mother with empty nest syndrome.

She'd love to be able to phone her at the nursing home and speak to her because she can't visit, but she can't phone because Biggy will get anxious and agitated and want to get home. This breaks my mum's heart.

It's life cycle stuff. Maybe it's time someone started the next generation and gave Mum and Anju Masi something new to do.

(I didn't say that. I really didn't say that. Did I?!)

Biggy always taught us to see the best in every situation. But what is good about the present? We are losing her day by day. And with her will go that wisdom, that unconditional love, that seemingly old-fashioned way of being …

Or will it? Every day I see this family getting stronger, I see Biggy's wisdom filtering through the generations and I see hope. Strangely, it takes a tragedy to happen before you realise how much someone means to you. The prospect of not having them in your life gives you a kick up the bum and makes you see that we have a finite time to make a difference. Biggy's dementia has taught me more about humanity, nurture, mental health and patient care than any textbook ever did. Through her illness, I have realised the value of family and of peace of mind. Through her illness, we have been given life. But that's Biggy through and through, wise as a sage, nondescript and unassuming. With a personality all of her own, one that won't ever leave us no matter what the dementia does.

Chapter 13

In the midst of all this chaos and confusion, when Big Mama was still in the rehab unit and I'd summoned up the courage to go and visit, she had a startling moment of lucidity. I was up there expecting the usual 'Have you eaten?' nonsense but instead I was taken completely by surprise.

'Just forgive your dad,' she said out of the blue. 'Let it go.' I'd heard this stuff before, but not for a long time. This was Big Mama in wise mode.

But then, 'The reason you don't want to have children,' she went on, 'is because you're scared.'

Well. You could have scooped me off the floor. She'd shut me up completely and no mistake. Once I'd got my breath back, I managed to joke 'Is it in my face? Is it that obvious?'

'You are. You're scared.'

'How do you know I don't want to have kids? I didn't tell you anything about anything,' I said, laughing. 'What are you on today?'

But she had hit the nail on the head. So I just sat there and listened to her while she told me all these anecdotes about when she was first married and what happened to her and about living in the joint family in Kenya and so on. It was the sort of stuff you'd expect from the head of your family and it had obviously been sitting there ready to be said for some time. It didn't come out as a lecture. She wasn't saying 'Marry, don't marry, do it this way, have this ceremony.' She was just giving me the benefit of her life's experience and passing on invaluable advice about how to live.

And then, just as I'm getting cosy and coming over all emotional, she said, 'There are people here in the centre who want to meet you. Come on and I'll introduce you.' Then she peeped round the corner and said 'There's Stephen's dad coming.' And of course it wasn't Stephen's dad because what would Stephen's dad be doing in a Rehab Unit? I realised with a jolt that actually she was back to being demented again.

I'd first met Stephen about five years earlier. I didn't introduce him and Big Mama that soon because there was no real need to, but we were officially engaged two years ago and the wedding will be in July this year. Less than six weeks from now as I write this.

I took him round to the sheltered flat in Arlington Street so they could give each other the once over. As usual she was all smiles and welcomes.

'What would you like to drink?' she said, showing him the inside of her pristine fridge.

'I'll have a Lucozade, thank you,' he said.

She handed him a bottle from the fridge. 'Here have the bottle. Do you want a glass?'

'No thanks,' he said, 'if you don't mind.'

'I don't mind at all,' she said.

Luckily there was quite a gathering there that day and everyone had plenty to talk about. But when it came time to leave and Stephen stood up to say his goodbyes and was just about to go out the door, she tapped him on the shoulder, laid an eye on the Lucozade bottle and held out her hand.

'Mine,' she said.

After we'd all stopped laughing, we were mortified. What was she doing? This was before we realised she had dementia.

You would think after this rather inauspicious beginning that she didn't like Stephen but you'd be wrong. She adores him.

She was at it again recently with her advice. Again I hadn't expected it. We were on a routine visit to see her only a couple of weeks ago.

'Not long to go now,' she said.

So I'm thinking, 'Not long to go to what?' I'm thinking she can't possibly remember about the wedding.

Then she said to me, 'Come here.'

I'm thinking, 'What's wrong now?'

'There's somebody in there,' she said. 'Looks like Stephen's dad.'

Ah, that old chestnut.

She lifted her Zimmer up and she pointed with it. It was this guy who looked like the exact double of Stephen's dad. I felt the hairs bristle on my neck.

'Your father-in-law's a very patient man,' she said, 'but then Stephen's very good. How is he? How's his work going? He's in such a good job. He's always helping people.'

I thought, 'How the hell do you know all this? Stephen should be the first to go.' But he's found a place in her heart and she was making herself remember.

'Just because he doesn't talk, doesn't mean you need to keep

166

babbling on,' she said.

At this of course I burst out laughing. I do babble on. It's what I do. There's no stopping me most days. So Big Mama laughed too, but actually she was serious. She had important things to tell me and she wasn't finished yet.

'It's a marriage,' she said. 'You've got a family and you're entering a family, a very good family too, a wonderful family. It's about compromise and about respect. It's not the minute that there's something wrong you walk out. And you don't say anything nasty. You don't shout at each other and you don't fight with each other. Just remember that it's the whole family that are involved and that we're giving them a daughter and that there's respect there.' And she proceeded to give me more stories about her fifty-three year marriage to Papa Ji, the stuff about Kenya and the joint family but all sorts of other things too.

'We never had any fallings-out in our marriage,' she said. 'It took a lot of compromise but, if he was ever in a bad mood I would try and pacify him, and, if I was ever in a bad mood, he'd try and pacify me. I learnt this early on. One time I was in a terrible bad mood for some reason, I can't remember why, and I'd made this meal for us to eat, but I was too annoyed to sit down and eat with him.

"I'm not eating with you,' I said, in a huff. 'You're a fool.' So he left me to my huff and sat down to eat.

"Mmm,' he said. 'This is delicious. Do you want to eat the food?'

'But still I refused.

"You don't want to eat the food?' he said. 'You're the one

missing out. This food's amazing. If you're going to cut off your nose to spite your face ... well, don't you eat it. That's fine. But why are you being in a huff and depriving yourself of food?'

'So I sat down and I ate and it was delicious and I thought, 'How stupid of me.''

'I got married very young, you know, Pinky,' she said. And off she went with more of this stuff. The advice was priceless.

I'm surprised every time when she asks about Stephen because I always expect her to have forgotten him completely. After all he's the last person *into* the family so you'd expect him to be the first person *out*.

'He's got such a good family,' she said. 'It doesn't matter if he doesn't speak the language. You are so happy and the wedding's next year.'

Ok, so she'd got the timing wrong but I was like, 'Oh-my-God where has this come from?'

But the worrying thing now is how she'll cope with the wedding and, more to the point, how we'll cope with her at the wedding.

'At the engagement she was good,' said my mum. 'People are still talking about her at the engagement.'

'But that was two years ago now,' I said.

'She was OK when Bala was here,' said my mum, persisting. 'All the other relatives will be here. She'll be fine with all those people round about her.'

I thought back to all those other occasions Biggy had been at in the last year. At Stephen's birthday she was fine. It was a big party and she didn't say much but she was happy, smiling to

168

everyone, very comfortable. Then, as recently as two months ago, Stephen's parents invited her for dinner as is traditional before a wedding. I thought it would be a disaster. How much of the conversation was she going to pick up? What was she going to understand or contribute? What would we talk about? But again she was chatty and delighted to be there as always, laughing and smiling, eating everything in sight.

'Sit down, sit down,' she kept saying to Stephen's dad. 'No man do work.'

He kept getting out the canapés and doing all the stuff, just generally getting on with it the way most guys would do, and we were all killing ourselves laughing and going, 'Stop it! Stop it!'

The wedding may not be so easy.

Most of the time she remembers about it. Other times not.

As you can imagine, with only six weeks to go there's a lot of talk on arrangements. During a recent trip to visit Deepa, Mum and I talked non-stop all the way to Manchester and non-stop all the way back about nothing but the wedding. In fact my ear was sore the next day.

During a visit to Biggy the other day we were all talking about the wedding.

'Whose wedding are you talking about?' she said.

'Pinky's wedding,' we said.

'Nobody told me,' she said. 'I wish somebody had told me. I can guide them and all that.'

This is the tradition. This is what the head of the family does, they guide the rest of us poor fools through the preparations and the ceremonies and the various rituals. Strictly speaking this should have been her job, except we aren't far off twice the age she was when she married, several decades have passed since then and we're in a different country never mind continent. But traditions are traditions. The difference is we mostly get to pick and choose which ones we want on this occasion.

'Yes, we did tell you,' said my mum. 'Pinky and Stephen. You remember?'

'Well, of course I still remember. I was just asking, just testing,' says Big Mama, embarrassed, of course, about forgetting.

Five minutes later, we had the same conversation again, word for word ... and five minutes after that, and again, and again. It was time to go home.

What is obvious is that Biggy may possibly be fine while the wedding is going on, but she may not. Also that she can't stay overnight in the hotel. Also that she will need a designated minder at all times because she can't be responsible for herself.

She is going to struggle for the whole day. One of the problems is that the venue is miles away from the nursing home, so who's going to take her back? Various people have been suggested but most of them are required at the wedding and we don't want her going back after a family wedding with someone who's not family.

We took Mum to Stobo Castle for a big birthday recently and made a total fuss of her. All the family were there except Big Mama. Talk often turned to the wedding.

'Maybe it's a good idea if Biggy doesn't come to the wedding at all,' said Mum during a private moment. 'It would make everything so much easier.'

I actually gasped. I had never considered the possibility of Big Mama not being at my wedding. Perhaps I'd never have allowed myself to think it, but this gave me permission.

'I need to talk to Stephen,' I said, blinking. I knew this was a huge thing for Mum to say. I needed time to catch up.

Stephen and I had several discussions about this but really I knew I'd be devastated actually, the way our relationships going, and the way I know Biggy feels about us getting married.

So we will have to find a way. And it won't be my mum's other suggestion, which is that she goes back to the nursing home with her in a taxi and then comes straight back.

'But you're the mother-of-the-bride!' I said, horrified. 'You can't leave the wedding. I need you. I need both my mums.'

This may seem strange but in Indian culture this is normal. It is a mark of how close my mum is with her sister Anju and an indication of how much involvement Anju Masi has always had in my life. 'Masi' means 'Auntie, but literally it means 'Little Mum'. Mum and Anju Masi are sharing the mother-of-the-bride role.

They are both, therefore, making preparations day and night, including both their houses having a total makeover and mountains of food being prepared in advance, special freezers being bought to keep it all fresh, certain brothers turning off said freezer so he can do something weird with his car and one hundred lovingly hand-prepared chapattis going completely to waste. Argh!

And so on.

Indian weddings usually go on over two or three days and

there will be family gatherings a-go-go with relatives arriving from all over the place. Everybody's already fighting for attention. 'I'm the bride (me!) I'm the groom (Stephen!) I've come from far away so I'm special in all of this. What's my job? My kids have to be included. What's their role? This has to be done, that has to be done. Why are you not doing it this way? Can I have gluten-free pakora and low-calorie gulab jamin?'

The only person who hasn't asked a single question or made any demands is Big Mama. And she's the head of the family!

But what if someone wants to take her place?

There is this hierarchical thing which happens in Indian families too. Maybe it happens in other cultures but for Indian families it's quite formalised. For me there is nobody who can take her place. Why would anybody need to? She's not dead. I don't want someone whom I wouldn't recognise if I saw them in the street, someone who doesn't know me.

My mum says she needs help with the rituals.

'What rituals?' I said. 'We've discussed what we're doing already.'

'You've just become so westernised, Pinky.'

Well, that was unfortunate. That's the quote that gets used very often. It's very emotive. Stephen was there at the time. We met eyes and I took a deep breath.

'That term will not get used around our house,' I said, 'and it will not get used around our children and it will not be used to describe the two of us.'

'I understand that, darling, but someone must have that place, out of respect for the family. It's what happens in Asian families.

172

You respect your elders.'

I hadn't realised how fiercely protective I was of Biggy's position until recently. Since that conversation, Preity and I have had long email chats and texts, usually headed 'Rant 1' or 'Rant 2'

'I'm sending you over rant number 35!'

'Received. I shall reply in a couple of hours.'

Most of it has been about the fact that I am so protective over Biggy and Nani Maa having their places as head of the family.

'She can fucking go to fuck if she thinks she's going to replace Big Mama,' I texted about this interloper, if you'll excuse my French.

'I'm giving you a virtual high five, girl,' Preity came back.

'If she says anything to Big Mama I'm going to take her to one side and tell her to butt out,' I said.

Preity and I are agreed on this. Nani Maa is still driving in her 80s. She still goes to see Biggy off her own bat and is forever phoning up and asking after her. They are like chalk and cheese but I know she'll look after her at the wedding. Bala Masi will too.

I don't do 'places' and I don't do status and I don't like hierarchy. I do real family relationships, the ones that matter: my siblings (I include my cousins in this), my mums and my two Grans. Big Mama is the person who brought me up, brought all of us up, in fact. All the kids are saying 'If anybody needs to get spoiled and if anyone needs to get pampered and clapped and consulted it's Biggy.'

She'll be sitting at the wedding just clapping and smiling. She'll be so happy without looking for any attention. It won't matter if she's given any accolade, although she will – or any special consideration, which will happen naturally. She'll be happy that her kids are happy and that her Grand-kids are happy. She doesn't need any special involvement for other people to realise she's important. She'll be there. There's no way she's not going to be there. Deepa's giving a speech and she's going to thank various people but I'm thinking she'll do a special thank you for my Gran.

Big Mama's the one who I've learnt most from. She's calmed me right down about all this. The things that psychiatry teaches you, text books and so on about reflective communication, all that can help. But here's an illiterate woman who doesn't speak much English and who's teaching me how to be a better doctor and to reflect on things and to 'just let things go'. Brilliant.

So the last time Mum, Stephen, Raj and I went to visit Biggy, I said 'Biggy, kee khenda Billy Connolly? What does Billy Connolly say?'

She passed Stephen a third Blue Riband biscuit and smiled at me. 'Billy Connolly?' she said. 'Who's Billy Connolly? Why would he be talking to me?'

Raj and I fell about laughing.

'Bloody fucking!' said Stephen.

'Oh!' said Big Mama.

I waited for Mum's sparks to fly.

'Bloody fucking!' said Biggy, before Mum could get a word in. 'Blood fucking! I knew that. I was just testing.'

I didn't know whether I wanted children or not, but now I think I want to have a child, because I want my child to see this woman.' My child needs to know who this woman is because of the wisdom that comes from her and the love that she will give this child.

Big Mama, I wanted to wake you up and have you see the world around you. I wanted you to see things my way and understand that times have changed, that your philosophies are outdated and obsolete. What you have shown me in your demented state is that I was the one who was sleeping. Life isn't truly worth living without the ups and down. Yes, it's a journey that you need to forge for yourself but the quality of that journey is enhanced by who you choose to walk with. You can't choose your family and for that, today, I am grateful. Wherever you are, whatever state you are in, I will not forget what you have taught me. Your mind will live on. Your ideas will make a difference and the dementia won't have beaten you, or our family. I look forward to our future, whatever it may bring. If you can still find time to smile over the little things then that is good enough for me.

Biggy – Kee Khenda

AFTERWORD

So I got married. And Biggy was there in her turquoise suit. She grabbed a lollipop from the candy cart and spent the afternoon out in the sun, beaming. She didn't remember the wedding the next day and gave Stephen and I lots of trouble for getting married without her.

And so life goes on. Biggy is continuing to get worse but the families are strengthening around her. She is losing weight and she is forgetting faces but in many ways she's still right there. We have to remember that she isn't our patient but she is our relative. There will be uncertainty and we have to face this with her, with dignity and respect.

Biggy has taught me the value of a life well-lived, by individual not social standards. She has taught me to respect each day, not because she is ill but because of who she was when she was well. In this respect my grandmother's spirit will live on – dementia or no dementia.

My advice to all those families thinking and feeling the same way is to communicate. Do not internalise the unacceptable feelings; do not feel guilty. It is only in processing the horrible emotions that someone can see the bigger picture. Spend time laughing with your loved ones, instead of quizzing them on what day it is. Try to facilitate their spirit to keep on going. It is only since doing this that I have found a measure of peace.

FACTS ON DEMENTIA

(from Alzheimer's Society)

Dementia describes different brain disorders that trigger a loss of brain function. These conditions are all usually progressive and eventually severe.

Alzheimer's disease is the most common type of dementia, affecting 62 % of those diagnosed. Other types of dementia include: vascular dementia (affecting 17% of those diagnosed) and mixed dementia (affecting 10% of those diagnosed).

Symptoms of dementia include memory loss, confusion and problems with speech and understanding. Dementia is a terminal condition.

There are 800,000 people with dementia in the UK with numbers set to rise to over 1 million by 2021. This is expected to soar to 1.7 million by 2050.

80% of people in care homes have dementia or severe memory problems.

There are over 17,000 people under 65 with dementia in the UK.

Dementia affects nearly 25,000 people from black, Asian and minority ethnic groups in the UK.

Unpaid carers, supporting someone with dementia, save the economy eight billion pounds a year.

Dementia is one of the main causes of disability later in life, ahead of cancer, cardiovascular disease and stroke.

There is no cure for Alzheimer's disease or any other type of dementia. Delaying the onset of dementia by five years would halve the number of deaths from the condition, saving 30,000 lives a year.

Dementia research is desperately underfunded. The government invests eight times less in dementia research than cancer research.

USEFUL NUMBERS AND WEBSITES

Alzheimer's Society
National Dementia Helpline: 0300 222 1122
enquiries@alzheimers.org.uk

Dementia UK
www.dementiauk.org
Tel: 020 7697 4160
Fax: 0845 519 2560
E-mail: info@dementiauk.org

Help for carers
www.carers.org

Age UK
www.ageuk.org
Tel: 0800 169 6565

All royalties received by the author from this book will be donated to Alzheimer's Society to help fund and support the research into and treatment of dementia.

Indigo Dreams Publishing Ltd
24, Forest Houses
Halwill
Beaworthy
Devon
EX21 5UU
www.indigodreams.co.uk